The Bread Book

by

Dale L. Morgan

edited by

Barbara A. Withers

Presbyterian Publishing House
Atlanta/Philadelphia

The Bread Book
LifePac: Bible
Celebrate

Published especially for use in:
Cumberland Presbyterian Church
Moravian Church in America
The Presbyterian Church in Canada
Presbyterian Church (U.S.A.)
Reformed Church in America

Art Director: Pat Steiner
Illustrator: Gloria Claudia Ortiz
Designer: Cindy Dolan

Printed in the United States of America

CONTENTS

CHAPTER 1

PROMISE

In the beginning, when God created the heavens and the earth, there was no one there to see it happen. But millions of years later, about six hundred years before Jesus was born, a Hebrew poet sat down by a river in Babylon and wrote about the creation of the universe with these words:

1 בְּרֵאשִׁ֖ית בָּרָ֣א אֱלֹהִ֑ים אֵ֥ת הַשָּׁמַ֖יִם וְאֵ֥ת הָאָֽרֶץ׃

But perhaps the English translation of these Hebrew words will be easier to read. It is found in the first chapter of the Bible in a book called Genesis, which means "beginnings."

"In the beginning God created the heavens and the earth. The earth was without form and void. Darkness was upon the face of the deep, and the Spirit of God moved over the face of the waters."

In the poet's vision, at the beginning of creation there was nothing but water—water everywhere—no light anywhere, and no air, except for the breath, or spirit, of God.

"And God said, 'Let there be light'; and there was light. And God saw that the light was good. And God separated the light from the darkness. God called the light Day, and the darkness God called Night. And there was evening and morning, one day."

The Hebrew poet is not bothered by the fact that the creation of light is mentioned before the creation of the sun. Those ancient people noticed that the earth became light even before the sun rose. And the earth stayed light even after the sun had disappeared over the horizon for the night. Therefore, they may have reasoned that on the first "day," or sometime in those early aeons of creation, God just created light, pure and simple light. God created light that took away the fearful darkness of those rolling, churning waters—light that in its simplest form was very, very good.

"And God said, 'Let there be a firmament in the center of the waters, and let it separate the waters from the waters.' And God made the firmament and separated the waters which were under the firmament from the waters which were above the firmament. And it was so. And God called the firmament Heaven. And there was evening and there was morning, a second day."

The Hebrew poet knew that something had to open up and separate all those deep, deep waters before the dry earth could be formed. So the poet imagined that God created a firmament, or heaven, clear in color and shaped rather like an upside-down bowl. When the waters above the bowl were separated from the waters below the bowl, an open space would appear between them. In that open space God could form earth. This enormous firmament would have windows in it. Every so often, when God opened the windows, the waters that were held above would fall upon the waters below—and it would rain.

"And God said, 'Let the waters under the heavens be gathered together into one place, and let the dry land appear.' And it was so. God called the dry land Earth, and the waters that were gathered together God called Seas. And God saw that it was good. And God said, 'Let the earth put forth vegetation, plants yielding seed, and fruit trees bearing fruit in which is their seed, each according to its kind, upon the earth. And it was so. And God saw that it was good. And there was evening and there was morning, a third day."

One of the most wonderful things about God's creation of the earth was that its creation would not end on that "third day" or any day thereafter. But the seeds of re-creation that God planted would continue to grow through the ages. So today at this very moment, seeds are growing somewhere that will produce flowers and fruits. These flowers and fruits contain more seeds which will grow and grow through all of earth's tomorrows.

"And God said, 'Let there be lights in the firmament of the heavens to separate the day from the night. And let them be for signs and for seasons and for days and for years.' And it was so. And God made the two great lights, the greater light to rule the day, and the lesser light to rule the night. God made the stars also. And God saw that it was good. And there was evening and there was morning, a fourth day."

Here at last the sun and moon are flung into the sky. But our Hebrew poet conceals their names by calling them the greater and the lesser lights. That is because, by the sixth century Before the Common Era, the time when this account was written down, the Hebrew people had been taken as captives to the land of Babylon. The Babylonian people worshiped the sun and moon as if they were gods. The Hebrews believed in one God. Living among people who worshiped false gods had always been a problem for the Hebrews (as seen in the following chapters). So the poet made certain that the reader would not even give a name to these lights.

According to the writer, God's purpose in creating the sun and the moon on this "fourth day" was not the fact that they gave light to the earth (remember, the pure light of the second day had already brightened up the darkness). It was because the sun and moon, by their rising and setting, created a calendar of seasons—days and months and years—by which time could be measured and crops could be grown. Without these measurements of day and night and month and year, one would not know when to plant corn, or even when to celebrate a birthday.

For the Hebrew people, the day ended when the sun set for the night. The next day began when the first stars were seen in the sky. That is why the poet, for each day, wrote: "evening and morning, one day"—and not the other way around.

"And God said, 'Let the waters bring forth swarms of living creatures. And let birds fly above the earth across the firmament of the heavens.' So God created the great sea monsters and every winged bird. And God saw that it was good. And God blessed them, saying, 'Be fruitful and multiply.' And there was evening and there was morning, a fifth day."

The Hebrew people did not like the sea very much. For one thing, they were farmers, not sailors. For another, they were often attacked by other tribes of people who came in ships across the Mediterranean Sea. And for yet another thing, they were convinced that there were sea monsters in the deep waters which could swallow alive an entire person.

But even if the Hebrews did not like the sea very much, they knew that in the beginning God must have blessed the creatures that swam in the sea, as well as the birds that flew through the air, for like the plants, they kept multiplying all on their own, season after season, year after year.

"And God said, 'Let the earth bring forth living creatures according to their kinds.' And it was so. Then God said, 'Let us make humankind in our image, after our likeness; and let them have dominion over the fish of the sea, and over the birds of the air, and over the cattle, and over all the earth.' So God created humankind in God's own image. Male and female God created them. And God blessed them, and said to them, 'Be fruitful and multiply, and fill the earth and subdue it. And have dominion over the fish of the sea and over the birds of the air and over every living thing that moves upon the earth.' "

After all life on earth had been created, including fish and birds, cattle and creeping things, God finally created human beings. And these human beings, both male and female, were said to be in God's image. That does not mean that God looks like men and women. It means, rather, that people were created to be and act like God.

God's care for all of creation was now to be humankind's care for all of creation. Men and women were to subdue or cultivate the earth so that it would produce the food necessary to keep creation going. They were to have dominion over fish and animal life in order to care for it.

"And God said, 'I have given you every plant yielding seed which is upon the face of all the earth, and every tree with seed in its fruit. You shall have them for food. And to every beast of the earth, and to every bird of the air, and to everything that creeps on the earth, everything that has the breath of life, I have given every green plant for food.' And it was so. And God saw everything God had made, and it was very good. And there was evening and there was morning, a sixth day."

Creation was so perfect, in those days of its beginning, that some people would call it "paradise." Another ancient writer of Genesis believed that when the first man and woman were created (the two people in this second Creation story became known as Adam and Eve), they lived in a perfect garden called Eden until, disobeying God, they were driven out of the garden and into a wilderness where they had to scratch for a living. But in the poet's vision of creation, everything was very, very good and living things multiplied so abundantly that there was no wilderness anywhere. Everything was perfect, so perfect that God could now rest awhile.

"And on the seventh day God finished the work which God had done. And God rested. So God blessed the seventh day and hallowed it, because on that day God rested from all the work which God had done in creation."

Hallowed means "set apart." Ever since people thought to do it, one day a week has been set aside to remember that, in the beginning, it was God who created the heavens and the earth and human beings and all that lives on the earth.

But, as the years went on, and as human beings continued to "be fruitful and multiply" over the face of the earth, there came a time when the people—though they may have hallowed the one day for God—forgot all about God on the other six days of the week. They forgot about how good the earth was and how God had blessed it and given them charge of it. They began to fight with one another, to steal one another's land and belongings, and even to kill one another—to snuff out the God-given breath of life. This made God very angry! So God looked, and finally found, a good and righteous man named Noah. Noah and his wife had three sons—Ham, Japheth, and Shem. Of all the people on the earth, only Noah and his family lived in fellowship with God.

God told Noah, "I have determined to make an end of all humankind;

for the earth is filled with violence through them. I will destroy humankind with the earth."

According to God's instruction, Noah and his family built themselves a boat, or ark, to ride out the storm. They took aboard the ark two of every kind of living thing so that the earth could be repopulated when the waters went down.

For God had said to Noah, "I will establish my covenant with you. I have seen that you are righteous before me in this generation."

And so it was, according to the Hebrew poet, that God opened the windows of heaven. The waters above, which had been separated from the waters below, fell down upon the earth. And rain fell upon the earth forty days and forty nights, drowning all beasts and people of the earth except for Noah and his family.

When at last the storm was over, Noah released some birds to see if there was a dry place to land the boat. A raven went forth and never came back. A dove went forth and came back, but showed no sign of having found land. Noah waited seven days (because that was how long it had taken God to create everything in the beginning) and he released another dove. The dove went forth and when it returned it carried an olive branch in its beak. At last there was a sign of dry land for Noah. And, through all the generations to come, and even to us, the dove would be a sign of peace. The dove with the olive branch meant that wars on earth and their violence had ended, and creation could begin again on land blessed by God for Noah, and his wife and children, and their flocks.

And God blessed Noah and his family, and said to them, "Be fruitful and multiply, and fill the earth. Every moving thing that lives shall be food for you." The blessed goodness of creation would never be forgotten by those who could remember the goodness of their Creator. And thus it was that when Noah looked up into the firmament, he had a new surprise. For suddenly, he saw in the sky something that had not been there when the world was first created but which would now always be there after a storm—a long, beautiful arc of spectacular colors: a rainbow, the sign of God's promise.

God said, "Never again shall all flesh be cut off by the waters of a flood. This is the sign of the covenant which I make between me and you and every living creature. When the bow is seen in the clouds, I will look upon it and remember the everlasting covenant between God and every living creature."

It is said that Noah and his wife told their children all about God's covenant of peace with all the people of the earth. And those children, when they grew up, told their children, too. And so the traditions about Creation and the flood, of re-creation and God's rainbow, were passed down generation after generation after generation.

Of course, some of the details got lost, and some new ideas were added, before the stories reached the Hebrew poet who, years and years later, wrote them down in Babylon. But the unchangeable truth of the stories was still there.

In the beginning, it was God who created the heavens and the earth, but in the end, it would be the people who would care for them. And when the people looked to the rainbow embracing earth and sky, they would remember how God had once blessed and loved them, knowing that God's love for all creation, and for those who care for it, would never ever change.

That was—that is—the promise.

CHAPTER 2

OBEDIENCE

The first stories in the book of beginnings, Genesis, are called prehistory because they came from a time before anyone knew how to write them down, and some of them even came from a time before there was anyone to write them down.

The later stories in Genesis which will be told in this chapter and the next could be called "how come?" stories. To the Hebrew people who read them, they answered questions like "How come our people are sometimes called Semites and sometimes Israelites and then again, Jews?" "How come from the beginning our people didn't get along with the Ishmaelites—the Arabs?" "How come, after the rainbow, there was a second sign of the covenant with God—circumcision—a ceremony when a Hebrew male child would have part of his own flesh cut to remember the promise of God?" "How come, from the very early days, the people of Israel did not sacrifice their firstborn sons to God the way people from other ancient tribes did?"

Here are some of the "how come?" stories from Genesis, the book of beginnings.

Noah, the good and righteous man God saved from the flood, had three sons. The youngest was Shem. As time passed, it became clear to the Hebrew genealogists (those people who kept track of family births) that it was the children and grandchildren of Shem who became a special people chosen by God. These people became known as the Shemites, or Semites. (In Hebrew, the symbols for "S" and "Sh" look alike.)

After Shem himself, the first important Semite was a man named

Abraham who was born in the land of Babylon nine generations after the flood. When Abraham's family moved north to Haran, in Mesopotamia, they had many flocks, servants, and household goods, a sign that they were very wealthy. Abraham also had a beautiful wife whose name was Sarah, but he had no children.

One day, when Abraham was seventy-five years old, he heard a voice saying: "Go from your country and your family to the land that I will show you. And I will make of you a great nation. I will bless you, and make your name great, so that you will be a blessing. And by you all the families of the earth shall bless themselves."

Abraham must have wondered how, in their childless old age, he and his wife Sarah could produce enough children to make a "great nation." But, convinced that this was the voice of God, he packed up his household and headed south from Haran toward Canaan, the promised land. Eventually, after a brief sojourn in Egypt, they arrived in Canaan and set up camp at Mamre. There under the sacred trees, Abraham built an altar and thanked God for bringing them to that place.

At first, everything went well for Abraham and Sarah in their new land. They had shade and plenty of water and grass for their flocks. Although neighboring tribes sometimes fought in Canaan, their battles did not involve the Semites and Abraham's family lived in peace.

But as the years went by and they had no child, Abraham began to question God's promise, saying, "O God, what will you give me, for I continue childless." And in a vision, Abraham heard God's voice in reply, saying, "Look toward heaven, and number the stars, if you are able to number them. So shall your descendants be."

Finally, Sarah, feeling the years of waiting and bitter disappointment, said to Abraham, "God has prevented me from bearing children. Go in to my slave. It may be that I shall obtain children by her." And, as the custom was in that time and place, Sarah's Egyptian slave, Hagar, became like a second wife to Abraham so that Abraham might have a child before he died.

When Hagar became pregnant, however, she boasted and bragged before Sarah. She treated Sarah's barrenness with contempt. And Sarah, jealous of Hagar's growing baby, became even more miserable than before. She said to Abraham, "May the wrong done to me be on you! I gave my slave to your embrace, and when she saw that she had conceived, she looked on me with contempt." Abraham, perhaps confused by Sarah's change of heart, replied, "Your slave is in your power. Do to her as you please."

Sarah then made Hagar so miserable that Hagar ran away from Mamre—and would have kept running all the way to the wilderness of Shur except that suddenly, like Abraham, Hagar too heard the voice of God. As she stopped to drink from a spring in the desert, Hagar looked up and saw an angel of God.

"Hagar, slave of Sarah, where are you going?" asked the angel.

"I am fleeing from my owner," replied Hagar.

"Return to your owner, and submit to her," said the angel. "I will so greatly multiply your descendants that they cannot be numbered. You are with child, and shall bear a son. You shall call his name Ishmael. He shall be a wild donkey of a man, his hand against everyone and everyone's hand against him; and he shall dwell over against all his relatives."

In those days people believed that if someone actually saw God face-to-face, that person would die right there on the spot. Hagar was amazed by what she had seen and heard.

"Have I really seen God and lived?" she asked.

When Ishmael was born, mother and son returned to Abraham's camp at Mamre where they became part of Abraham's household once more.

Ishmael grew up. At thirteen, he was still an only child. By this time, Sarah was ninety and Abraham was ninety-nine. But then, one day, Abraham again heard the voice of God. "I am God Almighty. Walk before me and be blameless. My covenant is with you, and you shall be the father of a multitude of nations. Sarah shall be a mother of nations. Rulers of nations shall come forth from her."

As one who comes before the altar of God, Abraham bowed his face to the ground, but suddenly, instead of praying, Abraham began to laugh. He said to himself, "Shall a child be born to a man who is a hundred years old? Shall Sarah, who is ninety years old, bear a child?" Abraham laughed and laughed and laughed.

Considering for a moment that Ishmael might finally be his official son and heir, Abraham made a practical suggestion to God: "O that Ishmael might live in your sight!"

But God replied, "No, Sarah your wife shall bear you a son. You shall call his name Isaac. I will establish my covenant with him as an everlasting covenant for his descendants."

This astonishing news of God's continuing promise of a child to a now very old couple had to be delivered also to Sarah. If Abraham himself had told her of his vision, she probably never would have believed it. And so it was that one hot afternoon, Sarah also was visited by messengers of God.

Abraham was sitting at the door of the tent and Sarah was busy inside. Suddenly, three men appeared at the door and Abraham, offering the traditional hospitality of the desert, saw to it that they were given food to eat and water to drink. After the men had eaten, they said to Abraham, "Where is Sarah your wife?"

Abraham answered, "She is in the tent."

"I will surely return to you in the spring," said one of the messengers, "and Sarah your wife shall have a son."

When Sarah overheard this, her reaction was the same as Abraham's had been. She laughed to herself. She laughed and laughed and laughed.

And she said, "Everyone who hears of this will laugh on account of me."
But the messengers heard her laugh and said to Abraham, "Why did Sarah laugh? Is anything too hard for God?"
In time to come, this sort of announcement from God, of the impending birth of a baby, would be called an *annunciation*. At the desert well, Hagar had received an annunciation about Ishmael. In later years there would be heavenly annunciations of the births of Samson, King Josiah, and John the Baptist. The best-known and best-loved annunciation would be the annunciation of the birth of Jesus as told by an angel to Mary of Nazareth.

After Abraham heard the annunciation concerning the birth of his son, Isaac, he was commanded to show his loyalty to God in a new way. The rainbow covenant, which promised that never again would God destroy creation, now demanded a response from the people. God said to Abraham: "Every male among you shall be circumcised. You shall be circumcised in the flesh, and it shall be a sign of the covenant between me and you. Every male throughout your generations, whether born in your house, or bought with your money, shall be circumcised. So shall my covenant be in your flesh an everlasting covenant."
That very day Abraham, Ishmael, and all Abraham's male slaves were circumcised to honor God.

The next year, Isaac was born. The name Isaac was an appropriate one, for Isaac, in Hebrew, means "laughter." At last, Sarah was happy. She told all her friends, "God has brought me joy and laughter."
But it was said that even after Isaac's birth, Sarah and Hagar still did not get along. One day, when Ishmael and Isaac were playing together, Sarah again became jealous. Ishmael and his mother Hagar were sent away to spend the rest of their lives in the wilderness. So Abraham's descendants resulted in two groups of people—the Israelites (Abraham's descendants through Isaac who eventually became known as Jews) and the Ishmaelites (Abraham's descendants through Ishmael who eventually became known as Arabs). Isaac was circumcised when he was eight days old. And on the day he was weaned, his parents gave a great feast. In all things, Sarah and Abraham, now more than ever, responded to God with total obedience.

One day, God tested Abraham to see how far this obedience would go. The story of the test is one of the most exciting stories in scripture. It is found in Genesis 22—and it goes like this.
In the land of Canaan, where Abraham and Sarah had settled, it was the custom among the Canaanite people to offer their "firstfruits" to their creator as a sacrifice in gratitude for an abundant harvest. Firstfruits included fruit, of course, and corn and grain and sheep and cattle—but it also included firstborn sons. Firstborn sons were the ones who would

carry on the family name, ensuring that the family wealth and power would stay with the male side of the family. (Daughters, when they married, joined their husband's families.) If the firstborn son, then, was offered back to God, this was seen by the Canaanites as a sign of their faith that God would send yet another son to carry that family into the future.

Thus it was that one day, when Isaac was still a young child, Abraham heard the voice of God say, "Abraham!"

And Abraham replied, "Here am I."

And God said, "Take your son, your only son Isaac, whom you love, and go to the land of Moriah. Offer him there as a burnt offering upon one of the mountains of which I shall tell you."

What must Abraham have thought? That God had reconsidered making Ishmael his heir? That God, who had given him a son at age one hundred, would do it again at one hundred and ten? Or that God had decided, after all, not to make Isaac's descendants as numerous as the stars in the sky?

The story, however, does not reveal Abraham's thoughts; it only tells of Abraham's obedience. Arising early the following morning, Abraham cut wood for the burnt offering, and tied it on the back of a donkey. He took two servants, and Isaac, and together they journeyed to the place God had told him.

After they had traveled three days on the road, Abraham saw the mountain up ahead. He said to his servants, "Stay here with the donkey. I and the boy will go over there and worship, and come again to you." Abraham took a sharp knife and a live, hot coal to start a fire and he handed the wood to Isaac.

Isaac said, "Here is the fire and the wood. Where is the lamb for the burnt offering?"

"God will provide the lamb for a burnt offering, my son," said Abraham.

When they came to the place of which God had told him, Abraham built an altar and laid the wood upon it. He tied Isaac's arms and legs and laid him upon the wood. And then Abraham took the knife and raised it high above Isaac, in order to kill his son with a single stroke.

At just that moment, Abraham heard a voice call his name: "Abraham! Abraham!"

"Here am I!" Abraham cried.

"Do not lay your hand on the boy or do anything to him," said the voice. "For now I know that you fear God, seeing you have not withheld your son, your only son, from me."

It must have been with great joy and a thankful heart that Abraham unbound Isaac. Then the two of them sacrificed a ram they found caught by his horns in a thicket. From that day on, Abraham called the place "God will provide."

And, from that day on, that is "how come" the descendants of Abraham would not sacrifice their firstborn sons to God, even though their Canaanite neighbors still did. The Canaanites thought they were sacrificing in obedience to God. But Abraham had learned that obedience means believing with all your heart that, no matter how impossible it may seem, in the end God will provide.

Through God's provision, Isaac was born in laughter to two very old people. And through God's provision, Isaac lived long enough to father two sons of his own—Esau and Jacob. These children of Abraham did not equal the number of stars in the sky—but this was only the genesis of God's story. This was only the beginning.

CHAPTER 3

BLESSING

From the beginning, Isaac's twin sons, Esau and Jacob, did not get along. Isaac's wife, Rebekah, said that they had even struggled with each other while yet in the womb. Esau, the firstborn son, was an outdoorsman. He tended flocks in the pastures around their home in Beer-sheba and was known as a good hunter. His skin was very hairy. Jacob, the second-born son, preferred to stay home in the tent helping his mother. Jacob's skin was very fair and smooth.

One day, when Esau came in from hunting and saw Jacob standing over a fire stirring lentil soup, he begged to have some.

"First sell me your birthright," said Jacob, eager to have the double share of inheritance Esau would receive as Isaac's firstborn son.

"I am about to die," said Esau. "What use is a birthright?"

"Swear to me first," said Jacob. And Esau did.

Years later, when their father, Isaac, was an old man and blind, he sent for Esau. "My son, I am old," said Isaac. "Take your arrows and your bow, and hunt game for me. Prepare for me savory food, such as I love, that I may eat it and bless you before I die."

Esau, favored by Isaac, went immediately to do as his father ordered. He believed with the people of his time that deathbed blessings carried enough power to guarantee a prosperous future to those who received them.

Rebekah overheard their conversation, however, and quickly called Jacob, the twin she loved. Then she told him of her plan. "Son, go to the flock, and bring me two good young goats, that I may prepare savory food for your father, such as he loves. And you shall bring it to your father to eat, so that he may bless you."

While the meat cooked, Rebekah helped Jacob dress in the clothes Esau wore when he worked outdoors tending the animals. She covered Jacob's hands and neck with goatskin so that, if Isaac should feel them, they would feel hairy to his touch.

When the meal was ready, Jacob took it to his father. "Who are you, my son?" asked Isaac.

"I am Esau, your firstborn," lied Jacob. "Now sit up and eat of my game, that you may bless me."

"How is it that you have found it so quickly, my son?"

"Because the LORD your God granted me success," said Jacob.

"Come near, my son," said Isaac, "that I may feel you, to know whether you are really my son Esau or not."

Jacob carefully stretched out hair-covered hands toward his father. His father felt his hands and declared, "The voice is Jacob's, but the hands are Esau's. Come near and kiss me, my son."

When Jacob came near, Isaac smelled his garments and finally was convinced that the son before him was not Jacob, but Esau. "See, the smell of my son is as the smell of a field which GOD has blessed!"

And so it was that Isaac gave the blessings of the firstborn son to Jacob.

Later, when Esau found out that Jacob had stolen the blessing that should have been his, he was enraged. He said, "The days of mourning for my father are approaching; then I will kill my brother Jacob."

Rebekah heard Esau's threat and quickly sent Jacob away. "Your brother Esau comforts himself by planning to kill you," she said to Jacob. "Flee to Laban, my brother in Haran, and stay with him awhile, until your brother forgets what you have done to him."

Jacob ran from Beer-sheba. When he got to Bethel, he lay down upon the ground to sleep, resting his head on a pillow of stone.

In a dream, Jacob saw a ladder above him, reaching all the way up to heaven, and angels going up and coming down on it. Then he heard a voice say: "I am the SOVEREIGN, the God of Abraham your father and the God of Isaac. The land on which you lie I will give to you and to your descendants. By you and your descendants shall all the families of the earth bless themselves."

Early the next morning, Jacob took the stone he had used for a pillow and, pouring oil on it, made an altar for God. And,thanking God for the blessing, he promised that as long as he lived he would give back to God as an offering one tenth of all his wealth.

Finally, Jacob arrived at his uncle Laban's home in Haran. This was the home his grandfather Abraham had left to go to Canaan years before. Laban, glad to see Jacob, fed him and set him to work tending his sheep and goats.

After a month, Laban decided that Jacob should be paid for his work.

He said, "Tell me, what shall your wages be?"

Jacob had noticed Laban's two daughters, Leah and Rachel. He had fallen in love with Rachel, and so he replied, "I will serve you seven years for your younger daughter, Rachel."

Laban agreed, and after seven years he gave a great wedding feast for his daughter and the hardworking bridegroom who had served him for so long. After the wedding, when the bride removed her thick veil, Jacob discovered that it was actually Leah whom he had married. He was furious and shouted, "What is this you have done to me, Laban? Did I not serve with you for Rachel? Why then have you deceived me?"

Laban explained, "It is not so done in our country, to give the younger before the firstborn."

It seemed that Jacob was being justly punished for deceiving his own father and for stealing the birthright of the firstborn son. But when Laban saw how unhappy Jacob was, he added, "Complete the marriage feast of this daughter, and we will give you the younger one also in return for serving me another seven years."

So Jacob also married Rachel whom he loved. And in time he became the father of a daughter, Dinah, and ten sons: Reuben, Simeon, Levi, Judah, Dan, Naphtali, Gad, Asher, Issachar, and Zebulun. But not one of these children was born to Rachel. Like Sarah, Rachel longed for a child. Like Hagar, Leah taunted her sister as she presented one baby after another to Jacob.

At long last, Rachel did have a baby, a boy she named Joseph. And, because Jacob loved Rachel with all his heart, Joseph became his father's favorite son.

Jacob, his wives, and all their children lived happily for many years. But, in time, Jacob began to feel bad about cheating Esau and decided to return to Canaan to ask for Esau's forgiveness.

Saying good-by to Laban, Jacob packed up his household and sent messengers on the road ahead of him with a message for Esau: "Thus says your servant Jacob: 'I have lived with Laban, and stayed until now. I have oxen, donkeys, flocks, menservants, and womenservants; and I have sent to tell my lord, in order that I may find favor in your sight.'"

The messengers did as they were told. When later they returned to Jacob, they reported, "We came to your brother Esau, and he is coming to meet you, and four hundred men with him."

Thinking that Esau had gathered an army to fight against him, Jacob was greatly afraid. He divided his entire household into two separate camps, thinking, if Esau comes to one camp and destroys it, then the other will escape.

Finally, Jacob prayed to God: "I am not worthy of the steadfast love and faithfulness which you have shown to your servant. I crossed the Jordan with only my walking stick; and now I have become two camps.

Please save me from my brother."

He also separated from the flocks a sizable gift for Esau: two hundred twenty goats, two hundred twenty sheep, and some camels, cattle, and donkeys. Jacob told the servants who ran ahead of the caravan to be sure to announce to Esau that, when he met Jacob, there would be many gifts awaiting him.

Then, in the silence of the night, Jacob led his wives and sons across the river Jabbok to the safety of the opposite shore. When Jacob went back across the river again and was alone on the other bank, suddenly a stranger appeared before him. This stranger wrestled with Jacob all night long. Finally, toward morning, when neither of them appeared able to win, the stranger touched Jacob's thigh and put it out of joint. Jacob, however, continued his tight hold on his opponent until the stranger cried, "Let me go, for the day is breaking!"

"I will not let you go," said Jacob, "unless you bless me."

"What is your name?" asked the stranger.

"Jacob."

"Your name shall no longer be called Jacob, but Israel, for you have striven with God and have prevailed."

In ancient Hebrew, the name Israel meant something like "one who strives with God." Although Jacob never knew the stranger's name, he was convinced that the opponent with whom he had wrestled all night was from heaven.

"I have seen God face-to-face," Jacob said (as Hagar had said years before), "and yet my life is preserved."

When Jacob opened his eyes after the battle and the blessing, he saw Esau coming toward him with his band of four hundred men. But instead of attacking Jacob, Esau ran to his brother, embraced him, and wept. Jacob wept, too, and he presented Esau with gifts.

Esau forgave Jacob and soon Jacob and his family settled nearby in the land of Canaan. Later, Rachel gave birth to yet one more son, named Benjamin. From the twelve sons of Jacob would now come people known as the twelve tribes of Israel. And that is "how come" the Semites in time were also called Israelites, or children of Israel. They were happy in Canaan until Rachel, Jacob's best-loved wife, died. After that, Rachel's firstborn son, Joseph, became even more important to Jacob.

One day, Jacob made Joseph a colorful coat with long sleeves, the sort of robe men wore when they were not working in the fields. But his brothers saw that Joseph was getting special treatment from their father and because of this, they began to hate him. They were angered further by Joseph's dreams.

"We were binding sheaves in the field," bragged Joseph one morning, "and my sheaf arose and stood upright. Your sheaves gathered round it, and bowed down to my sheaf."

"Are you to reign over us?" his brothers asked.

They hated him more for his dreams and his words. And Joseph had another dream. "In another dream," said Joseph, "the sun, the moon, and eleven stars were bowing down to me."

When Jacob heard of Joseph's dreams, he said, "What is this dream that you have dreamed? Shall I and your mother and your brothers indeed come to bow ourselves to the ground before you?"

Jacob wondered about Joseph's dreams and kept them in his mind. But the brothers were very jealous.

One day, when they were all with the flocks in Dothan, Joseph's brothers plotted to kill him. "Here comes this dreamer," they said to one another. "Come now, let us kill him and throw him into one of the pits. Then we shall say that a wild beast has devoured him. We shall see what will become of his dreams."

But before they could take Joseph's life, a caravan of traders passed by on the way to Egypt. This gave one of the brothers an idea.

"Come, let us sell Joseph to the Ishmaelites. Then our hand will not be on our brother."

So they sold Joseph for twenty shekels of silver. After they had dipped his colorful robe in animal blood, the brothers told their father, Jacob, that Joseph had been killed by wild animals. Jacob mourned the death of his son for many days, refusing to be consoled.

The merchants took Joseph to Egypt where they sold him to the captain of the guard. For a time, Joseph served the guard well. But one day, charged with a crime he did not commit, Joseph was arrested and put into prison. But because God was with him, Joseph found favor with the prison guard. Soon Joseph was helping to care for other prisoners. He told the prisoners about God. Praying for God's guidance, Joseph helped them to understand the meaning of their dreams. After several years in prison, Joseph became so famous an interpreter of dreams, that even Pharaoh heard of him—and sent for his help.

"I have had a dream, and there is no one who can interpret it," Pharaoh said to Joseph. "I have heard it said of you that when you hear a dream you can interpret it."

Joseph answered, "It is not in me. God will give Pharaoh a favorable answer."

"In my dream, I was standing on the banks of the Nile. Seven cows, fat and sleek, fed in the reed grass. Seven other cows came up after them, poor and very gaunt and thin, such as I had never seen in all the land of Egypt. And the thin and gaunt cows ate up the seven fat cows. I also saw in my dream seven ears growing on one stalk, full and good. And seven ears withered, thin, and blighted by the east wind, sprouted after them, and the thin ears swallowed up the seven good ears."

When Joseph heard Pharaoh's dreams, he said, "God has told you what will happen. There will come seven years of great plenty throughout all the land of Egypt. After them there will arise seven years of famine. Now you should choose a man discreet and wise, and set him over the land of Egypt. And let other officials gather all the food of these good years as a reserve against seven years of famine which are to come to the land of Egypt."

So Pharaoh said to Joseph, "Since God has shown you all this, there is none so discreet and wise as you are." Then Pharaoh took his own signet ring and put it on Joseph's hand. He put a gold chain around Joseph's neck. He gave Joseph a chariot to ride and when he passed by, the people shouted, "Make way! Make way!"

Because of Joseph's leadership, after the seven years of plenty had come and gone, the people of Egypt still had enough food to survive the seven years of famine.

But back in the land of Canaan, Jacob and Joseph's eleven brothers and all their households and flocks began to starve.

When Jacob learned that there was grain in Egypt, he said to his sons, "Why do you look at one another? I have heard that there is grain in Egypt. Go down and buy grain for us there."

Because Joseph was the ruler from whom all grain was to be bought, the brothers came to him. And as the dreams had predicted, they bowed down before him. Because Joseph was dressed as an Egyptian ruler, they did not recognize him. However, Joseph recognized his brothers, but treated them like strangers. He spoke roughly to them. "Where do you come from?" he asked.

"We, your servants, are twelve brothers," they replied, "the sons of one man in the land of Canaan. The youngest is this day with our father, and one is no more."

Joseph remembered the dreams he had dreamed of his brothers. "You are spies!" he shouted. "Bring your youngest brother to me so your words will be verified, and you shall not die." But Joseph saw to it that their bags were filled with grain and that the money they used to pay for it was replaced in each sack.

The brothers returned home and presented the corn to Jacob. They told him that the Egyptian had ordered Benjamin to go next time they needed grain. Jacob, firmly opposed, said: "My son shall not go with you, for his brother, Joseph, is dead, and Benjamin only is left. Why did you tell the man you had another brother?"

His sons answered, "The man questioned us carefully: 'Is your father still alive? Have you another brother?' Could we in any way know that he would say, 'Bring your brother down?' Now, send the boy with us." Finally, Jacob agreed, and once more the brothers bowed down to Joseph in Egypt.

When Joseph saw his brother Benjamin, he secretly wept. Then he ordered his servant to take his silver cup (the one that he used divining dreams) and to place it in Benjamin's sack of grain.

As the sons of Jacob were traveling back to Canaan, Joseph's steward overtook them and accused Benjamin, "Why have you returned evil for good? Why have you stolen my silver cup? Is it not from this that my lord drinks, and by this that he divines? You have done wrong."

The brothers were arrested and returned to Joseph for trial. Again, they bowed and one of them pleaded, "Let me be your slave and let the boy go back with his brothers. How can I go back to my father if the boy is not with me?"

And Joseph said, "I am your brother, Joseph, whom you sold into Egypt. God sent me before you to preserve for you a remnant on earth, and to keep alive for you many survivors. You shall dwell in the land of Goshen. Make haste and bring my father down here."

Joseph threw his arms around his brother Benjamin and they both wept. Then Joseph embraced all his brothers and wept some more.

Jacob and all the brothers' wives and children arrived in Egypt. And there Jacob lived for seventeen years before he died. When the time came for Jacob to give a deathbed blessing, as his father Isaac had given him, Joseph appeared before him with his own two sons. The older son was Manasseh and the younger Ephraim. As Jacob stretched out his hands in blessing, he crossed them and put his right hand on the head of the younger son, giving Ephraim the greater blessing.

Joseph's two sons would become heads of two tribes of Israel, replacing Joseph himself and another brother, Levi, who would become an ancestor of priests, a group of people called Levites. The tribe of Ephraim turned out to be more important than the tribe of Manasseh, just as Jacob, in the end, turned out to be more important than Esau—and Rachel more important than Leah—and Isaac more important than Ishmael. By them, according to God's promise, all nations of the earth would bless themselves.

And that is how Genesis, the book of beginnings, ends.

CHAPTER 4

LIBERATION

Liberation means freedom from bondage, that is, being set loose from imprisonment, enslavement, or oppression. The second book of the Bible is called Exodus because it describes the way God liberated the Israelites from slavery in Egypt and helped them exit back to Canaan.

Four hundred years after the time of Joseph, there came to power an Egyptian pharaoh who wanted to destroy the Hebrew people. For one thing, as God had promised, the children of Abraham and Sarah now seemed as numberless as the stars in the sky and the sand by the sea—and Pharaoh thought that was too many Hebrews! And for another, Pharaoh feared that these numberless Hebrews might unite with Egypt's enemies along the borders of the frontier, and thus overthrow Egyptian power.

Pharaoh said, "Come, let us deal shrewdly with them, lest they multiply and, if war befall us, they join our enemies, and fight against us and escape from the land."

Pharaoh called in the Hebrew midwives, Shiphrah and Puah, and commanded them, "When you serve as midwives to the Hebrew women, if the baby is a son, you shall kill him. But if it is a daughter, she shall live." The two midwives, however, were faithful to God. And all the babies, both male and female, lived.

Then Pharaoh commanded all his people, "Every son that is born to the Hebrews you shall cast into the Nile."

When Jochebed and Amran, descendants of Jacob's son, Levi, had a baby—and it was a boy—they hid him where the soldiers would not find him. But when the baby was three months old and could be hidden no longer, his mother made a watertight basket, put him in it, and sent it floating down the Nile River toward the place where Pharaoh's daughter swam daily. The baby's sister, Miriam, hid in the bulrushes and watched to see what would happen.

When the basket floated near, Pharaoh's daughter opened it and exclaimed, "This is one of the Hebrews' children!" But instead of following her father's orders to drown him, the princess picked up the crying baby and held him close. In great relief, Miriam came out of hiding and suggested, "Shall I go and call you a nurse from the Hebrew women to nurse the child for you?"

Pharaoh's daughter agreed. "Go," she said. So the young woman went and called the child's mother.

So it was that the Hebrew baby, now given the name Moses, was raised by his own Hebrew mother until he was weaned and was then raised as a prince in the Egyptian court until he became a man.

One day, after he was grown, Moses left his palace and, for the first time, saw the hard labor the Egyptians laid upon the Hebrew people. He even saw a Hebrew worker beaten to death. Moses was so angry that he killed the Egyptian and hid the body. The next morning Moses saw two Hebrews fighting one another.

"Why do you strike your fellow?" he cried.

"Who made you a prince and judge over us?" one of the men asked. "Do you mean to kill me as you killed the Egyptian?"

Moses was suddenly afraid, and with good reason, for when Pharaoh learned that Moses had killed an Egyptian, Pharaoh sought to kill Moses. So Moses left the palace and ran for his life. He ran all the way to Midian where he found refuge and a new home. He married a woman named Zipporah and became a shepherd.

The years passed. Then, one day when Moses was grazing his sheep at Mt. Sinai, God and Moses spoke to one another in one of the most famous conversations in all of scripture. It began when Moses suddenly saw a bush that was burning—not an unusual sight, but this bush was not consumed by the fire.

"I will turn aside and see this great sight," Moses said, "why the bush is not burnt."

When God saw Moses approach the bush, God called to him: "Moses! Moses!"

And Moses answered God with the same words used by Noah and Abraham and many of the prophets yet to come. "Here am I."

"Do not come near," said God. "Take off your shoes from your feet, for the place on which you are standing is holy ground. I am the God of Abraham, Isaac, and Jacob, the God of Sarah and Rebekah and Rachel."

Moses took off his sandals and hid his face, for he was afraid to look at God.

Then God said, "I have seen the affliction of my people who are in Egypt, and have heard their cry because of their taskmasters. I know their sufferings. I have come down to deliver them out of the hand of the Egyptians, and to bring them to a good land, a land flowing with milk and honey. I will send you to Pharaoh that you may bring forth my people out of Egypt."

Moses was amazed and afraid. "Who am I," he asked, "that I should go to Pharaoh?"

"I will be with you," assured God.

In those days, the people of Egypt worshiped many different gods. So Moses asked, "If I come to the people of Israel and say to them, 'God has sent me to you,' and they ask me, 'What is God's name?' what shall I say to them?"

God's answer to this question became one of the greatest religious mysteries of all time. The original Hebrew words are hard to express in English, but if God had answered Moses in English, the answer would have sounded something like this: "I AM WHO I AM. Say this to the people of Israel: 'I AM has sent me to you.'"

Although the people never quite understood what the name 'I AM' meant, they knew that it was God's own powerful name, too powerful to be spoken by any of God's creatures.

Then Moses protested. "But they will not believe."

God said, "What is that in your hand?"

"A rod," said Moses.

"Cast it on the ground," said God.

Moses cast it on the ground and suddenly his rod became a snake.

"Put out your hand and take it by the tail," God commanded, "that they may believe that GOD—the God of their ancestors—has appeared to you!"

Moses had often watched the magicians of Egypt hypnotize snakes until they became as stiff as sticks, but he had never before seen a stick become a snake. He put out his hand, and when he touched the snake, it turned into a stick again.

But Moses still sought an excuse not to go to Pharaoh.

"Oh, my Lord," he said, "I am not eloquent. I am slow of speech and of tongue. Send some other person!"

This last excuse by Moses made God very angry. "Is there not Aaron, your brother? I know that he can speak well. You shall speak to him and put the words in his mouth. And you shall take in your hand this rod, with which you shall do signs."

Finally, Moses obeyed God and he and Aaron called together the Israelite leaders in Egypt. Moses did the signs and Aaron spoke the words God had given to them. The people believed Moses and Aaron and they bowed their heads to worship.

When Moses and Aaron went before Pharaoh, they said, "The God of the Hebrews has met with us. Let us go a three days' journey into the wilderness and sacrifice to GOD."

Pharaoh was so angered by Moses' and Aaron's request that he gave this order to the Hebrew taskmasters: "You shall no longer give the people straw to make bricks. Let them go and gather straw for themselves. But the number of bricks shall by no means lessen. For they are idle. Therefore they cry, 'Let us go and offer sacrifice to our God.' Let heavier work be laid upon the men, and pay no regard to lying words."

The burdens laid upon the Hebrews were so oppressive that the people cried in anger to Moses and Aaron: "You have made us offensive in the sight of Pharaoh and his servants. You have put a sword in their hand to kill us."

But God reassured Moses, "I appeared to Abraham, to Isaac, and to Jacob. I also established my covenant with them, to give them the land of Canaan. I have heard the groaning of the people of Israel whom the Egyptians hold in bondage and I have remembered my covenant. Go in, tell Pharaoh, king of Egypt, to let the people of Israel go out of his land."

And that is what Moses and Aaron did. Time and time again, they went before Pharaoh and told him that God wanted the Hebrews set free. Pharaoh refused to let them go, even though God sent great misfortunes, called plagues, upon the Egyptian people.

First, the Nile River, held sacred by the Egyptian people, turned to blood. Then frogs and gnats and flies and locusts invaded the land. All the cattle belonging to the Egyptians died, and the people broke out with hideous boils. There were terrible storms, with hail and thunder, and finally, one day, the sky became dark as night and remained dark for three days. Pharaoh, who believed that the sun itself was a god, was very upset when it seemed to disappear from the sky. But he was not upset enough to let the Hebrews go.

So God said to Moses, "Yet one plague more I will bring upon Pharaoh and upon Egypt. When he lets you go, he will drive you away completely. Tell all the congregation of Israel to take a lamb without blemish and on the fourteenth day of this month kill their lambs in the evening. Then they shall take some of the blood and put it on the two doorposts and the lintel of their houses. That night they shall eat the lamb's flesh, roasted, with unleavened bread and bitter herbs. It is GOD'S passover. For I will pass through the land of Egypt that night. I will smite all the firstborn in the land of Egypt. The blood shall be a sign for you, upon the houses where you are. And when I see the blood, I will pass over you. This day shall be for you a memorial day. You shall observe it forever."

When Moses had explained God's commands to the people, he added, "When you come to the land which GOD will give you, you shall keep this service. And when your children say to you, 'What do you mean by this service?' you shall say, 'It is the sacrifice of GOD'S passover.'" And the people bowed their heads and worshiped.

When the firstborn sons of the Egyptians lay dead, Pharaoh and the other Egyptians ordered Moses and the Israelites to leave the country quickly. As they left in haste, there was no time for the Israelites' bread dough to properly leaven. Miriam, Moses' sister, and the other women wrapped the dough in the folds of their long skirts and ran. Moses also took with him the bones of Joseph, son of Jacob and Rachel, for burial in the land of his birth. When the people traveled by day, a pillar of cloud went before them. And when they traveled by night, a pillar of fire was their guide. Thus God led the people to the shore of the Red Sea.

At the sea, the Israelites looked back and saw all Pharaoh's horses and chariots and warriors coming. The Israelites were afraid. "Is it because there are no graves in Egypt that you have taken us away to die in the wilderness?" they asked Moses.

"Fear not," Moses answered. "Stand firm, and see the salvation of GOD! GOD will fight for you, and you have only to be still."

Then, as God had commanded, Moses took up his rod and stretched it out over the sea; and suddenly a strong east wind began to blow, and the waters of the sea were pushed back. The Israelites were able to cross over the bottom of the sea on dry land. But when the Egyptians tried to follow, their horses and chariots stuck in the mire. Then when the winds ceased and the waters came together, Pharaoh and all his troops were drowned.

Liberation had come at long last to the Hebrew people. Miriam, the sister of Aaron and Moses, took up a timbrel and there, on the shore of the sea, she and the other women danced and sang:

> "Sing to GOD, for God has triumphed gloriously;
> The horse and the rider God has thrown into the sea."

After this celebration, the people began their journey into the wilderness that separated Egypt from the land of Canaan. Along the way, Moses found springs of water for them to drink and God provided food for them—quail and manna, a sweet edible substance the people called "the bread of the wilderness."

After three months they came to Mt. Sinai, where Moses had first heard God speak from the burning bush. Once again, God called Moses to come up the mountain. God said, "Thus shall you tell the people of Israel: You have seen what I did to the Egyptians, and how I bore you on eagles' wings and brought you to myself. Now therefore, if you will obey my voice and keep my covenant, you shall be my own possession among all peoples. For all the earth is mine, and you shall be to me a kingdom of priests and a holy nation."

Then God instructed Moses how the people were to appear before their God: "Let them wash their garments, and be ready by the third day. When the trumpet sounds a long blast, they shall come up the mountain."

On the morning of the third day, there was a thick cloud on the mountain. There were flashes of lightning and the sound of thunder. Then God spoke to Moses and gave him the laws by which the people of God were always to live. The first of these laws came to be known as the Ten Commandments.

1. I am the LORD your God, who brought you out of the land of Egypt, out of the house of bondage. You shall have no other gods before me.
2. You shall not make for yourself a graven image. You shall not bow down to them or serve them.
3. You shall not take the name of the LORD your God in vain.
4. Remember the Sabbath day, to keep it holy. Six days you shall labor, and do all your work; but the seventh day is a sabbath to the LORD your God. In it you shall not do any work.
5. Honor your father and mother.
6. You shall not kill.
7. You shall not commit adultery.
8. You shall not steal.
9. You shall not bear false witness against your neighbor.
10. You shall not covet your neighbor's house; you shall not covet your neighbor's wife [or husband], or manservant, or womanservant, or ox, or donkey, or anything that is your neighbor's.

There were other laws given to the Hebrews also which came to be written not only in the book of Exodus, but also in Leviticus, a book explaining how God was to be worshiped, and in the book of Deuteronomy.

After God had spoken these laws, Moses went up the mountain and stayed there forty days and forty nights. While he was gone, the people feared for their safety and so they said to Aaron, "Make us gods, who shall go before us. We do not know what has become of Moses, the man who brought us out of Egypt."

Aaron obeyed the people by taking all their jewelry and making from it a golden calf. The people danced around the calf, chanting, "These are your gods, O Israel, who brought you up out of the land of Egypt!" And they offered upon an altar burnt offerings to the golden calf.

Just then, Moses came down the mountain, carrying with him the two great tablets of the law. When he heard the singing and saw the people dancing around the golden calf, Moses threw the tablets down upon the stony ground and broke them.

"You have sinned a great sin," he told the people. "Now I will go up to GOD. Perhaps I can make atonement for your sin."

Once again, God met Moses on Mt. Sinai and gave him tablets of laws by which the people were to live.

After forty days, when Moses descended the mountain for the second time, the people looked and saw that his face was shining from being in the presence of God and they turned away in fear. Soon, however, Moses had all the workers appear before him to be instructed in the building of an ark to carry the covenant of God. The ark was not like Noah's, built for the flood, but was a box with wheels for pulling across the wilderness. Into the ark went the tablets of the law, the new covenant God had made with the people. Moses also instructed the workers to build a tent of God's presence where the ark would stay when the people encamped and where they could worship God.

But as the people continued their journey toward Canaan, they faced natural hardships and enemies who tried to kill them. Time and again they complained to Moses, "Would that we had died in the land of Egypt! Or would that we had died in this wilderness. Why does GOD bring us into this land to die by the sword?"

When Moses took their complaints to God, he learned that, because of their lack of faith, God would keep the people in the wilderness for forty long years. And while the children would live long enough to enter their new homeland, only two of the adults would remain alive to see that day—Joshua, a good warrior who was Moses' second-in-command; and Caleb, his brave friend.

One day, the people took a census to see how many Israelites were encamped in the wilderness. (The census, and the wilderness stories, are written in the book called Numbers.) And then God said to Moses: "Take Joshua the son of Nun, a man in whom is the spirit, and lay your hand upon him; cause him to stand before the priest and the whole congregation and commission him as your successor."

Moses did as God commanded and Joshua became the new leader who would lead the people into their promised land.

When Moses ascended Mt. Pisgah and looked down at the land below, he heard the voice of God saying, "This is the land which I swore to Abraham, to Isaac, and to Jacob. I have let you see it with your eyes, but you shall not go over there."

And the book of Deuteronomy, which tells about the death of Moses, ends with these words: "So Moses the servant of GOD died there according to the word of GOD. No one knows the place of his burial to this day. And the people of Israel wept for thirty days. And there has not arisen a prophet since in Israel like Moses, whom GOD knew face-to-face, none like him for all the signs and the wonders which GOD sent him to do in the land of Egypt."

The great prophet, Moses, died, knowing that at last he had led the people of God from bondage in Egypt to liberation in their promised land.

CHAPTER 5

NEW BEGINNING

After Moses died, God said to Joshua: "Arise, go over this Jordan. As I was with Moses, so I will be with you." And the people agreed that, as they had followed Moses, so they would now follow Joshua.

When they arrived near Jericho, Joshua sent in spies to explore the land. Word of this soon reached the king of Jericho, however, and he sent his own men throughout the city to search them out. The spies quickly found refuge in the home of a prostitute named Rahab. She took them up to her rooftop and covered them with stacks of flax, saying "I know that GOD has given you the land, and that the fear of you has fallen upon us. For we have heard how GOD dried up the water of the Red Sea before you when you came out of Egypt. As soon as we heard it, our hearts melted, because of you; for the LORD your God is God in heaven above and on earth beneath. Now then, swear to me by GOD that as I have dealt kindly with you, you also will deal kindly with my father's house, and deliver our lives from death."

The spies, seeing that she was faithful to God, promised to protect Rahab. They gave her a scarlet cord to hang from a window to signal Joshua's army that her house should be spared.

When the king's men arrived to search for the spies, Rahab told them, "Men came to me, but I did not know where they came from; and at dark, they went out. Pursue them quickly, for you will overtake them."

Later, when the king's men had gone far from the city, and all of Jericho was asleep, Rahab let the spies down from her roof by a rope. Then, in her window, she tied the scarlet cord.

The spies returned safely to Joshua's camp and the people of God prepared themselves to go up against Jericho.

God instructed Joshua: "You shall march around the city, all the men of war going around the city once. Thus you shall do this for six days. And seven priests shall bear seven trumpets of rams' horns before the ark. And on the seventh day you shall march around the city seven times, the priests blowing the trumpets. And when they make a long blast with the ram's horn, as soon as you hear the sound of the trumpet, then all the people shall shout with a great shout; and the walls of the city will fall down flat."

The inhabitants of Jericho must have been amazed, and then confused, and then terrified by this daily trumpeting processional around the walls of their city. When Joshua's troops finally let out a great shout on the seventh day, everyone inside the city walls ran for their lives, everyone, that is, except Rahab and her family. As the blood on the doorposts of their homes in Egypt had saved the Hebrews from death, so the scarlet cord in Rahab's window now saved her from the Hebrews. Rahab lived as one of the Israelites. Their genealogists wrote that she became the mother of Boaz, who married Ruth. If that is true, then it was from Rahab that Israel's greatest hero and king descended—for her great-great grandson would be David of Bethlehem.

Joshua and all the survivors of the wilderness experience at last had come into their promised land. As Joshua's army conquered more and more cities, word of their victories went before them and the inhabitants of the land were afraid. Cities fell before them and thirty-one Canaanite kings were put down from their thrones.

God commanded that the land be divided and that each tribe which descended from Jacob's sons be given territory of its own in which to live. And so there was territory set apart for the tribes of Reuben, Simeon, Judah, Issachar, Zebulun, Dan, Naphtali, Asher, Gad, Benjamin, and the descendants of Joseph's sons, Ephraim and Manasseh. Because the descendants of Levi were priests, they were not to own land, but each Levite family was assigned a city in which to live.

Finally, Joshua became too old to lead the people. At Shechem, where the bones of Joseph finally were laid to rest, Joshua made a new covenant between Israel and God, saying: "Choose this day whom you will serve, whether the gods your ancestors served in the region beyond the River, or the gods of the Amorites in whose land you dwell. As for me and my house, we will serve GOD."

The people promised, "Far be it from us that we should forsake GOD, to serve other gods! We will serve the LORD our God!"

Joshua set aside a large stone as a memorial to remind the people of their covenant. "It shall be a witness against you," he said, "lest you deal falsely with your God."

Joshua died (his life and death are recorded in the book of Joshua).

From then on the people's welfare rested on leaders known as judges. Three of the most famous were Deborah, Gideon, and Samson. Here are their stories from the book of Judges.

There was a Canaanite king named Jabin who had nine hundred iron chariots led by a wicked commander-in-chief named Sisera. For twenty years he ruled the land with great cruelty and oppression. Deborah, a woman of the tribe of Ephraim, was the judge of her people then—in fact, she was called not only judge, but also prophet. One day, Deborah sent for Barak, commander of Israel's army, saying, "The LORD, the God of Israel commands you, 'Go, gather your men at Mount Tabor, taking ten thousand from the tribe of Naphtali and the tribe of Zebulun. And I will draw out Sisera, the general of Jabin's army, to meet you by the river Kishon with his chariots and his troops. I will give him into your hand.'"

But Barak said to Deborah, "If you will go with me, I will go. But if you will not go with me, I will not go."

Deborah agreed, prophesying, "I will surely go with you. Nevertheless, the road on which you are going will not lead to your glory, for GOD will send Sisera into the hand of a woman."

Deborah, Barak, and ten thousand Israelites attacked the Canaanites at the foot of Mt. Tabor. Because God was with them, the Israelites were strong. When they had killed all of Sisera's men, he ran away. Sisera came to the tent of a woman named Jael. She welcomed him saying, "Have no fear."

"Please, give me a little water to drink," Sisera asked her, "for I am thirsty."

Jael gave him some milk and then made a place for him to rest.

"Stand at the door," Sisera commanded, "and if any man comes and asks you, 'Is anyone here?' say no." But as he slept, Jael drove a tent peg into Sisera's head, killing him.

And so it was that Sisera fell into the hand of a woman while Barak and Deborah, in the strength of their God, thoroughly defeated the Canaanite troops. When the battle was over, like Miriam at the Red Sea, Deborah and the people sang a victory song.

"In the days of Shamgar, son of Anath,
  in the days of Jael, caravans ceased
  and travelers kept to the byways.
The peasantry ceased in Israel, they ceased
  until you arose, Deborah,
  arose as a mother in Israel.
Awake, awake, Deborah!
  Awake, awake, utter a song!
  March on, my soul, with might!"

And because the people were once again worshiping God, the story of Deborah concludes with these words: "The land had rest for forty years."

But then the people of Israel once more sinned against God and God let the Midianites rule over them for seven years. When the Israelites planted crops, the Midianites would destroy them. They would steal Israel's livestock so the people had nothing to live on. One day, Gideon, a man of the tribe of Manasseh, was threshing wheat in a wine press, so the Midianites would not see him. An angel of God appeared to him and said, "GOD is with you, you mighty man of valor! Go in this might of yours and deliver Israel from the hand of Midian. Do not I send you?" Said Gideon, "How can I deliver Israel? I am the least in my family."

Because Gideon doubted that what the angel said was true, he made up a test. And because Gideon doubted his own strength, the angel made up a test for him, too. Gideon's test went like this.

"I am laying a fleece of wool on the threshing floor. If there is dew on the fleece alone, and it is dry on all the ground, then I shall know that you will deliver Israel by my hand, as you have said." In the morning, when Gideon squeezed the wool it was full of water, but the ground was dry all around. Then Gideon reversed the test. "Let it be dry only on the fleece. On all the ground let there be dew." And in the morning, it was so.

Now convinced that his mission was from God, Gideon gathered thirty-two thousand men to go to war against the Midianites. But then the angel of God said, "The people with you are too many for me to give the Midianites into their hand, lest Israel say, 'My own hand has delivered me.' Now therefore announce to the people, saying, 'Whoever is fearful and trembling should return home.'" When Gideon did as God had commanded, twenty-two thousand soldiers returned home!

But God said, "The people are still too many. Everyone that laps water with their tongue, as a dog laps, you shall set by themselves. Likewise everyone that kneels down to drink."

Gideon took the men to the river to drink and three hundred lapped the water like dogs.

"With the three hundred that lapped I will deliver you," said GOD to Gideon, "and give you the Midianites into your hand." In this way, Gideon knew that his strength was from God.

Later that night, Gideon divided his three hundred men into three companies. He gave them torches covered with clay jars so that the flames could not be seen. He also gave each man a trumpet. "Look at me," he said, "and do likewise. When I blow the trumpet, then blow the trumpet also on every side of the camp. And shout, 'For GOD and for Gideon.'"

As soon as the Israelites had encircled the Midianites' camp, Gideon broke his clay jar and blew his trumpet. At this signal, all three hundred men did the same, shouting, "A sword for GOD and for Gideon!" When the

Midianites heard the noise and saw the three hundred torches, they thought they were surrounded by thousands of Israelite soldiers. They ran in confusion throughout the camp, and in the dark many were killed by their own comrades. Eventually, all the Midianites were driven from the land.

After the battle, the Israelites asked Gideon to rule over them, but Gideon told the people, "I will not rule over you, and my son will not rule over you. GOD will rule over you."

And then, as the writer of the book of Judges put it, "The land had rest forty years in the days of Gideon."

But then, once again, "the people of Israel again did what was evil in the sight of GOD." And God let the Philistines rule over Israel for forty years. The Philistines were such a strong presence in those days that the land was soon named for them—Philistia or Palestine. One day an angel of God appeared in Zorah to the wife of Manoah and announced: "You shall conceive and bear a son. No razor shall come upon his head, for the boy shall be a Nazirite (one dedicated to God) from birth. And he shall begin to deliver Israel from the hand of the Philistines."

When the child was born his parents named him Samson. The boy grew and God blessed him and God's spirit strengthened him.

When he was grown, Samson fell in love with a Philistine woman and decided to marry her. As Samson was on his way to visit this woman, he came upon a lion. In his great strength, Samson tore the lion apart with his bare hands and left the carcass by the side of the road. The next time he passed that way, there was a swarm of bees in the lion's carcass and it was dripping with honey. Samson must have known that eating from a dead carcass would break his Nazirite vows of purity, but he ate some honey anyway. He continued to his bride's house where he gave a great feast to celebrate their marriage, as was a custom among young men.

"Let me now tell you a riddle," Samson told his thirty guests. "If you can tell me what it is, within the seven days of the feast, then I will give you thirty linen garments and thirty festal garments."

"Tell your riddle, that we may hear it," they said to him.

Samson said, "Out of the eater came something to eat. Out of the strong came something sweet."

The riddle was so hard that by the fourth day the guests had become desperate. They said to Samson's wife, "Entice your husband to tell us what the riddle is, lest we burn you and your father's house with fire."

And so she wept, saying to Samson, "You do not love me. You have told a riddle to my people, and you have not told me what it is."

Because his wife wept the seven days that their feast lasted, Samson finally told her the answer to his riddle. She promptly told her people and they said to Samson, "What is sweeter than honey? What is stronger than a lion?"

Samson was angry that he lost the contest and so he killed thirty Philistines, stole their linen and festal garments, and gave them to the men who had answered his riddle. Then he left his wife and went back to his parents' home.

Later, when his anger had cooled, Samson returned to the Philistine village with a gift for his wife. There he discovered that her father had given her away to another man. Samson's earlier anger did not compare to his fury over this. He burned the Philistines' fields and crops to the ground.

To retaliate, the Philistines killed Samson's wife. So Samson killed more Philistines. Then the Philistines began to take revenge on the people of Judah. To protect themselves, the Judahites bound Samson and turned him over to the Philistines. With his great strength, however, Samson broke the bonds that held him, picked up from the ground the jawbone of a dead donkey, and used it to overcome his Philistine captors.

For the next twenty years, Samson was a judge in Israel. But the Philistines never forgot their anger. One day, Samson again fell in love with a Philistine woman named Delilah. Seeing a new opportunity for revenge, the lords of the Philistines came to Delilah and said, "Entice him, and see where his great strength lies, and by what means we may overpower him, that we may bind him to subdue him. We will each give you eleven hundred pieces of silver."

Delilah tried to discover how Samson could be captured. Three times she begged to know the secret of his strength. Three times he answered, but when she tested his answers she found he was teasing her.

Finally, Delilah cried, "How can you say, 'I love you,' when your heart is not with me? You have mocked me these three times, and you have not told me where your great strength lies." And, at last, to put the matter to rest, Samson confided to Delilah the great secret of his strength.

"I have been a Nazirite to God from my mother's womb," he said. "A razor has never come upon my head. If I be shaved, then my strength will leave me, and I shall become weak, and be like any other man."

That night, while Samson slept, Delilah had the seven locks of his hair cut off. Then she awakened him, shouting, "The Philistines are upon you, Samson!" But because the strength of his dedication to God had left him, Samson was as weak as any other man. And so it was that the Philistines finally took Samson captive. They blinded him, and locked him up in their prison in Gaza. Months passed. And, as they passed, Samson's hair began to grow back. The day of the Philistines' festival to the pagan god, Dagon, arrived, and all the people gathered in Dagon's court to rejoice.

Samson, with his hair now fully grown, was brought from prison and forced to stand between two pillars so that the Philistines might make sport of him. But Samson put his hands on the pillars and prayed, "O Lord GOD, please remember me, please strengthen me, only this once."

Pushing his hands hard against the pillars, Samson shouted, "Let me die with the Philistines!" The temple crashed down upon Samson and thousands of his enemies.

Thus it was, according to the writer of the book of Judges, that "the dead whom Samson slew at his death were more than those whom he had slain during his life."

The story of Samson ends in victory, but like most of the stories of Joshua and the judges, it is a victory through violence.

One other special story of these times is in the book of Ruth. It is not a story of violence, but of love.

Naomi and Elimelech of Bethlehem, and their two sons, had gone to the country of Moab to find food during a famine. While there, the sons married Moabite women. One of them was Ruth. When all three of the men died, Naomi decided to return alone to Bethlehem. But Ruth begged to return to Bethlehem with her, saying, "For where you go, I will go, and where you lodge I will lodge; your people shall be my people and your God my God."

So Naomi agreed and when they arrived in Bethlehem, Ruth set to work gathering grain left behind for the poor in one of the recently-harvested fields.

Ruth brought the grain to Naomi, who exclaimed, "Where did you gather all this grain?"

"The man with whom I worked is Boaz," Ruth answered.

"Blessed be GOD!" exclaimed Naomi. "The man is one of our nearest relatives."

In those days it was the custom that the closest unmarried male relative would marry his brother's widow in order to keep her and her children, if she had any, in the family. So that night, Naomi told Ruth to go to the threshing place and to ask Boaz to marry her. Ruth did as she was told and Boaz gladly agreed.

In time, Ruth and Boaz had a son. They named the child Obed; he was the father of Jesse, the father of David.

Thus it was that two foreign women became part of the heritage of Israel and of the family of David: first Rahab, then Ruth.

The last sentence of the book of Judges is this: "In those days there was no king in Israel. Everyone did what was right in their own eyes." There would be yet one final judge and he would anoint the first king. The judge's name was Samuel. Because it took two full scrolls to tell Samuel's story, the books which tell about his life are called "first" and "second" Samuel.

Like so many who had lived before him, Samuel's birth was the answer to his mother's prayers. Hannah had said to God, "O GOD of hosts, if you will give to your womanservant a son, then I will give him to GOD all the days of his life, and no razor shall touch his head." (In other words, Hannah's son, like Samson, would be a Nazirite.)

And, in due time, Samuel was born. His mother, keeping her vow to God, delivered Samuel to Eli, the priest, and she praised God.

"My heart exults in GOD;
God raises up the poor from the dust,
and lifts the needy from the ash heap,
to make them sit with princes and inherit a seat of honor."

One night, Samuel was sleeping in the temple and he heard a voice calling, "Samuel! Samuel!"

Samuel, thinking it was the voice of Eli, ran to him and said, "Here I am, for you called me."

But Eli said, "I did not call. Lie down again." The same thing happened a second time, and a third. Suddenly Eli realized that the one calling Samuel was God. "Go, lie down. And if God calls you, say, 'Speak, LORD, for your servant hears.'"

Samuel followed Eli's instructions and God spoke to Samuel saying, "I am about to do a thing in Israel, at which the ears of everyone who hears it will tingle."

In the morning, Eli insisted that Samuel tell him all that God had said. Samuel told Eli that because Eli's sons had dishonored God, and because Eli had done nothing to stop them, they would all be cut off from Israel forever.

The next time that Israel went against the Philistines, the sons of Eli were killed and the ark of God's covenant was captured. When a messenger brought this news to Eli, the priest fell over backward from his seat beside the gate and because he was old and fat, the fall broke his neck and he died.

God continued to be revealed to Samuel at Shiloh. Like Deborah, Samuel became known not only as a judge, but as a prophet. And while Samuel was in charge, the Philistines no longer attacked Israel. As the biblical writer put it, "The hand of GOD was against the Philistines all the days of Samuel."

Finally, when Samuel was advanced in years, the people said to him. "You are old. Appoint for us a king to govern us like all the nations."

When Samuel prayed to God about this, God said: "Listen to the voice of the people in all that they say to you. They have not rejected you, but they have rejected me from being king over them. Only you shall solemnly warn them, and show them the way of the king who shall reign over them."

Samuel did warn the people as God directed. And then he anointed a king to rule over them. From wanderers in the wilderness had come a people who would soon become a great nation. The people of God had made a new beginning.

CHAPTER 6

UNITY

Although it was said that "from his shoulders upward, he was taller than any of the people," Saul, the first king of Israel, was a very weak ruler. He had once been a strong warrior, uniting Israel's tribes. But he disobeyed God, and God's spirit left him. The prophet Samuel mourned that the man he had anointed king had failed to lead the people.

But God said to Samuel, "How long will you grieve over Saul, seeing I have rejected him from being king over Israel? I will send you to Jesse the Bethlehemite, for I have provided for myself a king among his sons."

When Samuel arrived in Bethlehem, Jesse had seven of his sons pass before him, but Samuel said, "GOD has not chosen these. Are all your sons here?"

"There remains yet the youngest, but he is keeping the sheep," Jesse said.

"Go and bring him back," ordered Samuel.

When David stood before him, Samuel heard the voice of God saying, "Arise, anoint David; for this is the one."

From that day, although the people still looked to Saul as their king, the spirit of God was with David. As he tended his sheep, David would play the harp and write psalms in praise of God.

> GOD is my shepherd, I shall not want;
> God makes me lie down in green pastures,
> and leads me beside still waters;
> God restores my soul.

News of David's musical ability traveled to the battlefield where King

Saul's army was encamped against the Philistines. One day, when Saul was troubled, he sent for David to play his harp. David's playing soothed Saul so greatly that he asked Jesse to let David remain in his service.

Thus it was that David was in Saul's camp the day the Philistine giant Goliath challenged Israel, saying: "Choose a man for yourselves. If he is able to fight with me and kill me, then we will be your servants."

David said to Saul, "I will go and fight this Philistine."

Saul protested that David was too young and inexperienced to fight against such might. But David described the way shepherds had to fight against lions and bears to protect their sheep. "GOD who delivered me from the paw of the lion and from the paw of the bear, will deliver me from the hand of this Philistine," he said.

"Go," said Saul, "and GOD be with you."

Refusing to wear the king's armor, David took only five smooth stones from the brook and his shepherd's sling and went to meet Goliath.

"Am I a dog, that you come to me with sticks?" shouted the giant.

"You come to me with a sword and with a spear and with a javelin. But I come to you in the name of the GOD of hosts," replied David.

Then David let a stone fly from his sling. It hit the giant in the head and he toppled over like a tree in the forest. When Saul and his men saw this, they shouted triumphantly. Saul's son, Jonathan, presented David with his own robe, battle armor, and sword, and the two young men made a covenant of friendship. Later Saul gave Michal, his daughter, to David in marriage.

David continued to win battles against the Philistines and Saul made him an officer in charge of his own troops. But one day, as they returned from a fight, Saul learned that David had become even more popular with the people than he. The women came from the cities, singing: "Saul has slain his thousands, and David his ten thousands." Saul was angry at this and was from then on jealous of David. Several times Saul tried to kill David, but David was rescued by Saul's own children, Michal and Jonathan.

One day, as David was playing his harp, Saul suddenly threw a spear at him, thinking to pin David against the wall. David quickly ducked, and then hurried back to his own quarters.

"If you do not save your life tonight," said Michal, "tomorrow you will be killed."

She let him down from a window and then padded their bed with pillows to make it look as if David were still there. Saul's messengers came in search of David, but Michal told them, "He is sick."

Then Saul threw back the covers and discovered that David was not there. He turned to his daughter and cried, "Why have you deceived me?"

For a time, David hid himself with Samuel. But, anxious to know when Saul's anger had cooled so that he might return home, David secretly met Jonathan in a field. Jonathan told David that Saul's anger had grown even worse and the two young men wept. "Go in peace," said Jonathan. "We have sworn both of us in the name of GOD, saying 'GOD shall be between me and you forever.'"

War between the Israelites and the Philistines continued and so did the war between the two anointed kings: Saul, from whom the spirit of God had departed, and David, who continued to grow in spirit and in popularity with the people.

One day, Saul returned from battle and his servants reported, "David is in the wilderness of En-gedi." Saul took three thousand of his men and went to seek him. As they traveled, Saul stopped at a cave to rest, not knowing that David and his followers had arrived there ahead of him and were hiding deep within its shadow.

Slowly David crept forward and quietly cut the bottom of Saul's robe. Later, as Saul left the cave, David followed him outside and showed him the piece of robe which he had cut.

"This day your eyes have seen how GOD gave you into my hand in the cave; but I spared you. I have not sinned against you, though you hunt my life to take it."

Saul wept and said, "Is this your voice, my son, David? You are more righteous than I. You have repaid me good, although I repaid you evil. And now, I know that you shall surely be king. The Kingdom of Israel shall be established in your hand."

Saul and David separated, but there was never peace between them. The Philistines continued to fight against Saul and finally conquered the Israelites at Mt. Gilboa. They killed Jonathan and his two brothers and a Philistine archer wounded Saul. Saul begged his armor-bearer, "Draw your sword, and thrust me through with it." But his armor-bearer refused, so Saul fell upon his own sword and died.

News of the death of Saul and Jonathan reached David and he sang a psalm of lament:

"Your glory, O Israel, is slain upon your high places.
  How are the mighty fallen!
Tell it not in Gath,
  publish it not in the streets of Ashkelon;
lest the daughters of the Philistines rejoice.

"Saul and Jonathan, beloved and lovely!
  In life and death they were not divided;
they were swifter than eagles,
  they were stronger than lions.

"How are the mighty fallen
  in the midst of battle!"

Even though the Israelite troops had lost Saul, their leader, they continued to fight against the Philistines—and against David. David set up his own government in Hebron and he lived there with his wives and the six sons who were born to him. One by one, the leaders of Saul's army were killed, and finally the leaders of Israel came to Hebron to make an alliance with David. They said, "We are your bone and your flesh." And, as Samuel had done before them, they anointed David king over all Israel.

David reigned from Hebron for seven years and then he finally conquered the last stronghold of enemy power, Jerusalem, and its high place, Mt. Zion. Though Bethlehem would always be the birthplace of his house and lineage, Jerusalem was now and forever named "the city of David." David ruled all Israel for thirty-three years. He brought the ark of God into the city, dancing before it in praise of God. David and all the Israelites celebrated with songs and harps and drums and cymbals.

The prophet Nathan proclaimed God's approval of David's reign. "Thus says the GOD of hosts, 'I took you from the pasture, from following the sheep, that you should be prince over my people Israel. I have been with you wherever you went, and have cut off all your enemies from before you. I will make for you a great name. I will appoint a place for my people Israel, and will plant them, that they may dwell in their own place, and be disturbed no more. When your days are fulfilled and you lie down with your ancestors, I will raise up your offspring after you. He shall build a house for my name, and I will establish the throne of his kingdom forever.'"

David had many sons by the women he had married, but none of these would succeed him as king. The birth of the son who would become king took place this way.

Late one afternoon, while David was walking on the palace roof, he looked across the courtyard and noticed a beautiful woman bathing in a pool. Her name was Bathsheba and she was married to a soldier named Uriah. David sent for Bathsheba and they become lovers. Later, when they discovered that Bathsheba was to have a child, David told the commander of his army, "Send me Uriah."

And when Uriah arrived, David said, "Go down to your house." Uriah would not go home, but camped with the soldiers at the door of David's house. David asked, "Have you not come from a journey? Why do you not go down to your house?"

Uriah answered, "The servants of my lord are camping in the open field. Shall I then go to my house, to eat and to drink, and to lie with my wife?"

So David told his commander, "Set Uriah in the forefront of the hardest fighting, and then draw back from him, that he may be struck down, and die."

When Bathsheba heard that Uriah was dead, she wept. Then David sent for her and she moved into his house and became his wife.

Soon after, the prophet Nathan went before David and told him a parable. "There were two men in a certain city, the one rich and the other poor. The rich man had very many flocks and herds. But the poor man had nothing but one ewe lamb, which he had bought. And he brought it up, and it grew up with him and with his children. It used to eat of his food, and drink from his cup, and lie in his bosom, and it was like a daughter to him. Now there came a traveler to the rich man, and he was unwilling to take one of his own flock to prepare for the traveler who had come to him. But he took the poor man's lamb, and prepared it for the man who had come to him."

David was angry. "The man who has done this deserves to die," he said.

"You are the man!" cried Nathan. "Why have you despised the word of GOD, to do what is evil in God's sight? Now therefore the sword shall never depart from your house. The child that is born to you shall die." Therefore the first son of David and Bathsheba died.

Bathsheba conceived again and the son she bore this time was the one who would succeed his father as king and who would build a house for God's name. His name was Solomon. Through David's other sons, however, Nathan's prophecy, "The sword will not depart from your house," came true.

One son, Amnon, molested his half-sister, Tamar, so her brother Absalom, in revenge, had Amnon killed. David first mourned the death of Amnon, but when Absalom fled for his own safety, David mourned Absalom's absence even more. Once away from his family, Absalom decided that he was old enough to replace his father as king of Israel. So he went to Hebron, where David's original kingdom had been proclaimed, and his followers announced, "Absalom is king at Hebron." David heard the strength of Absalom's following and ordered his own people to leave Jerusalem and flee for their lives. David himself went up the Mount of Olives, barefoot and crying with grief while Absalom entered Jerusalem and established his reign.

After many months, David's troops finally met Absalom's in battle. Absalom was riding a mule and when he rode under a large oak tree, his head caught in the branches—but the mule kept running. Absalom slid from the saddle and was left hanging by his hair. Joab, one of David's men, took spears and stabbed Absalom in the chest, killing him.

A messenger brought word to David of Absalom's death, announcing, "Good tidings for my lord the king! For GOD has delivered you this day from the power of all who rose up against you."

David asked, "Is it well with the young man Absalom?"

The messenger replied, "May the enemies of my lord the king be like that young man."

When David understood that his son was dead, he went up to the chamber over the city gate and mourned loudly, "O my son Absalom, my son, my son Absalom! Would I had died instead of you, O Absalom, my son, my son!"

There were occasional uprisings from David's other sons, but when it came time for David to die, he called Solomon to him and appointed him successor to the throne. "I am about to go the way of all the earth. Be strong, and show yourself a man, and keep the charge of the LORD your God as it is written in the law of Moses, that you may prosper in all that you do and wherever you turn."

When David died, he had ruled Israel for forty years.

After the two scrolls, or books, of Samuel, the Bible contains four scrolls, or books, called Kings and Chronicles. These books tell what happened from the time of King Solomon until the capture of Jerusalem when the Kingdom was no more. (The other books of the Hebrew scriptures are writings of prophets who lived during these times—and psalms that were sung as the people worshiped God—and proverbs they liked to tell their children.)

The continuing story of the Kingdom goes like this: Shortly after Solomon began to rule Israel, God appeared to him in a dream. "Ask what shall I give you," said God.

Solomon replied, "Give your servant an understanding mind to govern your people, that I may discern between good and evil. For who is able to govern this your great people?" God was pleased with Solomon's answer.

"Because you have asked this," God said, "and have not asked for yourself a long life or riches, I now do according to your word. I give you a wise and discerning mind, so that none like you has been before you and none like you shall arise after you. I give you also what you have not asked, both riches and honor, so that no other king shall compare with you all your days."

One day, two women appeared before Solomon, asking him to judge their case. Both claimed to be the mother of the baby boy they brought with them. Solomon said, "Bring me a sword! Divide the living child in two, and give half to the one, and half to the other."

The real mother cried, "Oh, my lord, give her the living child, and by no means slay it."

But the other mother said, "It shall be neither mine nor yours. Divide it."

Solomon judged, "Give the living child to the first woman, and by no means slay it. She is its mother."

When the people of Israel heard of Solomon's decision, they marveled, for they knew that the wisdom of God was in him.

As the name of his harp-playing father, David, had become attached to the psalms, so now Solomon's name became attached not only to the psalms, but also to the book of Proverbs, proverbs like these:

> A wise son makes a glad father,
> but a foolish son is a sorrow to his mother.
>
> Treasures gained by wickedness do not profit,
> but righteousness delivers from death.
>
> A slack hand causes poverty,
> but the hand of the diligent makes rich.

Solomon's kingdom grew, and so did his household. Eventually, he had seven hundred wives and three hundred concubines. To feed his court for just one day, Solomon needed one hundred and fifty bushels of flour, three hundred bushels of meal, ten stall-fed cattle and twenty pasture-fed cattle, a hundred sheep, and assorted other animals such as deer, gazelles, and poultry.

The times remained peaceful and finally Solomon decided, "Now the LORD my God has given me rest on every side. There is neither adversary nor misfortune. And so I purpose to build a house for the name of the LORD my God, as GOD said to David my father, 'Your son, whom I will set upon your throne in your place, shall build the house for my name.'"

Solomon sent to Lebanon for logs of cedar wood. He had great slabs of stone quarried nearby. Carvers decorated the walls with flowers and gourds. The entire inside of the temple—including the floor—was covered with gold. In the Holy of Holies, where the ark of the covenant was to be kept, two golden-winged cherubim were set in place to guard it. There were altars where fruits and grains and animals could be offered to God.

And when the ark was brought into the temple, a cloud suddenly filled the room. Solomon prayed to God: "I have built you an exalted house, a place for you to dwell in forever."

It had taken seven years for Solomon to build the temple. He also built a palace in Jerusalem and he repaired the cities of Hazor, Megiddo, and Gezer.

The queen of Sheba, hearing of Solomon's achievements, paid him a visit and said, "The report was true which I heard in my own land of your affairs and of your wisdom. But I did not believe the reports until I came and my own eyes had seen it. And the half was not told me. Blessed be the LORD your God, who has delighted in you and set you on the throne of Israel!" The queen of Sheba presented Solomon with a gift of five tons of gold and more exotic spices than had ever been seen in Israel.

Solomon was now very wealthy, but his wealth came from the people he served—or rather, those who served him. He received twenty-five tons of gold every year in taxes and tributes, plus an additional percentage of all trade. Solomon's wealth, and their own increasing poverty, made the people very angry.

Then Solomon began to worship false gods—Ashtoreth, Milcom, and Chemosh. On the mountain east of Jerusalem, he built a temple for their worship. This made God angry.

"Since you have not kept my covenant and my statutes, I will surely tear the kingdom from you and will give it to your servant. Yet for the sake of David your father I will not do it in your days, but I will tear it out of the hand of your son."

One of Solomon's servants was named Jeroboam. Solomon had put him in charge of all the forced labor in the territory of the tribes of Ephraim and Manasseh. One day, on the road to Jerusalem, Jeroboam met the prophet Ahijah. Ahijah was wearing a new robe, but he took off his robe and tore it into twelve pieces, saying, "Take for yourself ten pieces. For thus says the LORD, the God of Israel, 'I am about to tear the kingdom from the hand of Solomon, and will give you ten tribes (but Solomon shall have but one tribe, for the sake of my servant David). You shall reign over all that your soul desires, and you shall be king over Israel.'"

When Solomon heard this, he tried to kill Jeroboam, but Jeroboam escaped into Egypt and stayed there until Solomon's death.

When Solomon died, he had reigned in Israel for forty years.

Rehoboam, Solomon's son, became king in Jerusalem. The ten tribes in the north sent to Egypt for Jeroboam to return home, and then they all entered the palace and stood before Rehoboam.

"Your father made our yoke heavy," they said. "Now therefore lighten the hard service and we will serve you."

But Rehoboam replied, "My father made your yoke heavy, but I will add to your yoke. My father chastised you with whips, but I will chastise you with scorpions."

When the ten northern tribes heard this, they shouted,

"What portion have we in David?
We have no inheritance in the son of Jesse.
To your tents, O Israel!
Look to your own house, David."

They made Jeroboam their king. Now there were two kingdoms in the land, a kingdom called Israel in the north with ten tribes and a kingdom called Judah in the south with just two tribes.

Never again would there be unity in the land promised forever to Abraham and Sarah and their descendants.

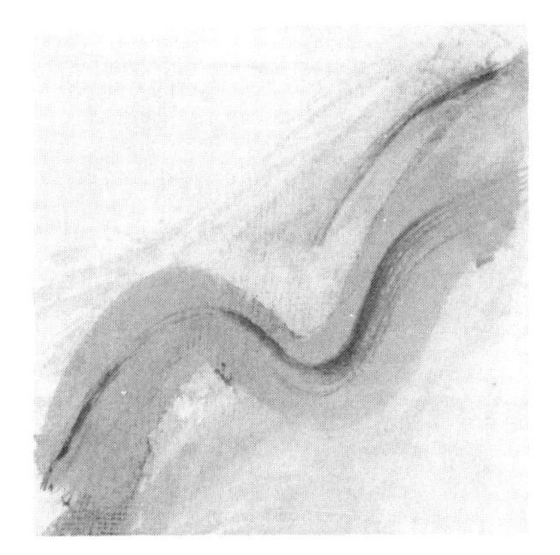

CHAPTER 7

DIVISION

In the north, King Jeroboam fortified the towns of Shechem and Penuel and began to rule the ten tribes. But the ark of the covenant remained in Jerusalem, in the Southern Kingdom of Judah, and Jeroboam said to himself, "Now the kingdom will turn back to the house of David, if this people go up to offer sacrifices in the house of GOD in Jerusalem."

So Jeroboam made two golden calves, the same sort of calves the Hebrews had worshiped in the wilderness of Sinai. He placed one in Bethel and the other in Dan, and told the people, "Here are your gods, O Israel, who brought you up out of the land of Egypt."

Jeroboam also built altars on the hilltops of Israel and he chose priests, not from the tribe of Levi, but from among the common people.

Ahijah, the prophet who had first foretold his kingdom, spoke again to Jeroboam. "Thus says the LORD, the God of Israel: 'I exalted you from among the people, and tore the kingdom away from the house of David and gave it to you. Yet you have not been like my servant David. You have done evil above all that were before you and have gone and made for yourself other gods. Therefore I will bring evil upon the house of Jeroboam.'"

And thus it was that when Jeroboam's son, Nadab, came to the throne, he was murdered by Baasha who then became king. And when Baasha died, and his son Elah became king, Elah was murdered by Zimri, who then became king. And when the people heard what Zimri had done, and they proclaimed Omri their true king, Zimri set the palace on fire and killed himself.

King Omri had to build a new palace, then, from which to rule, so he bought a hill from a man named Shemer. There he built a city and named it Samaria.

When Omri died, his son, Ahab, became king. According to the biblical writer, all the kings of Israel had been evil in God's sight, but Ahab was the most evil of all. He married Jezebel, a princess of Sidon, and worshiped her fertility gods, Baal and Asherah.

Unlike the days of David and Solomon in the south, there would be no hero-kings in the north. Instead, the biblical writers would tell of hero-prophets. The greatest prophet of the north was Elijah of Tishbe. He was a strange-looking man, dressed in animal skins with a belt made of hide. Elijah had a way of seeming to suddenly appear from nowhere to proclaim the Word of God. The first time Elijah appeared to Ahab, he said, "As the LORD the God of Israel lives, there shall be neither dew nor rain these years, except by my word."

Saying this, Elijah disappeared. But the message, though brief, was clear. Queen Jezebel's gods of fertility would be powerless before the God of Creation. And Elijah knew that the God who brought forth life in the beginning also had the power to take it back.

When, indeed, the rains ceased and drought began, God said to Elijah, "Depart from here and turn eastward, and hide yourself by the brook Cherith. You shall drink from the brook, and I have commanded the ravens to feed you there."

Elijah obeyed God and every morning and evening ravens brought food to him as the brook slowly died from lack of rain. When the brook finally was dry, God said to Elijah, "Arise, go to Zarephath, which belongs to Sidon, and dwell there. I have commanded a widow there to feed you."

At the gate to Zarephath, Elijah saw a woman gathering wood.

"Bring me a little water," he said, "that I may drink." And as she was going to bring it, Elijah added, "Bring me some bread."

At this, the woman exclaimed, "I have nothing baked, only a handful of meal in a jar, and a little oil in a cruse. And now, I am gathering a couple of sticks, that I may go in and prepare it for myself and my son, that we may eat it, and die."

Hearing the widow of Zarephath—in Jezebel's home country of Sidon—affirm that the God of Israel lived, Elijah must have known for certain that she was the one to whom God had sent him.

"Fear not," he assured her, "go and do as you have said. But first make a small loaf and bring it to me. Afterward make some for yourself and your son. For thus says the LORD the God of Israel, 'The jar of meal shall not be spent, and the cruse of oil shall not fail, until the day GOD sends rain upon the earth.'"

The widow, trusting Elijah and his promise, did as he had told her. All three of them ate that day and in the days that followed, yet somehow their flour and oil never ran out.

But suddenly one day, the widow's son got sick and died.

"What have you against me, O man of God?" she demanded. "You have come to me to bring my sin to remembrance, and to cause the death of my son!"

Elijah did not reply, but he sadly took the boy and carried him to the upper room and laid him upon his own bed. There Elijah cried to God, "O LORD my God, have you brought calamity even upon the widow with whom I am staying, by killing her son?" And then stretching himself upon the boy, Elijah cried out, "O LORD my God, let this child's life come into him again."

The boy revived and Elijah carried him down to the arms of his mother. "See, your son lives," he said.

The widow rejoiced as she took back her son, and she proclaimed that Elijah was, after all, God's true prophet. "Now I know that you are a man of God."

In the third year of the drought, God commanded Elijah to return and announce that rain would soon come. When Ahab saw Elijah again, he said, "Is it you, you troubler of Israel?"

"I have not troubled Israel," said Elijah, "but you have, and your father's family, because you have forsaken the commandments of GOD and followed the Baals. Now therefore send and gather all Israel to me at Mt. Carmel, and the four hundred and fifty prophets of Baal and the four hundred prophets of Asherah."

All of the Israelites and all of Jezebel's prophets gathered at Mt. Carmel. Elijah said to the people, "How long will you go limping with two different opinions? If the LORD is God, follow God; but if Baal, then follow him. I, even I only, am left a prophet of GOD. But Baal's prophets are four hundred and fifty men. Let two bulls be given to us. Let them choose one bull for themselves, and cut it in pieces and lay it on the wood, but put no fire to it. I will prepare the other bull and lay it on the wood, and put no fire to it. And you call on the name of your god and I will call on the name of GOD. The God who answers by fire, that one is God."

The prophets of Baal prepared their bull and began to chant, "O Baal, answer us!"

At noon, they were still chanting. Elijah mocked them, saying, "Cry aloud, for he is a god. Either he is daydreaming, or he is on a journey, or perhaps he is asleep and must be awakened."

By midafternoon, when fire still had not come to their altar, the priests of Baal began to cut themselves with swords and lances, for this, too, was part of their ritual.

Then Elijah called the people of Israel to come closer. He took twelve stones, one for each of the twelve tribes, and built an altar to God. Around the altar, he dug a trench. When this was done, Elijah told the people to pour water on his sacrificial bull. Three times they poured water until the altar was drenched with it and the trench was full. Then Elijah prayed to God: "O LORD, God of Abraham, Issac, and Jacob, let it be known this day that you are God in Israel, and that I am your servant, and that I have done all these things at your word. Answer me, O LORD, answer me, that this people may know that you, O LORD, are God, and that you have turned their hearts back."

Suddenly, from the cloudless sky, lightning flashed and fire fell upon Elijah's altar. It consumed the wood, the dust, the stones, and even dried up the water in the trench. When the people saw the fire, they fell to the ground and cried, "The LORD is God! The LORD is God!"

In the laws of Deuteronomy, it was written, "If a prophet says, 'Let us go after other gods,' that prophet shall be put to death, because he has taught rebellion against the LORD your God who brought you out of the land of Egypt." To obey the law, Elijah had the prophets of Baal put to death. Then he told Ahab, "Eat and drink, for there is a sound of the rushing of rain."

Elijah and his servant went to the top of Mt. Carmel to watch for clouds across the sea. Rain did come as Elijah had predicted, but so did a message from Jezebel. Ahab had told her about the death of the prophets and she warned Elijah, "So may the gods do to me, and more also, if I do not make your life as the life of one of them by this time tomorrow."

It was time for Elijah to disappear again and this time he ran all the way to the wilderness of Sinai. For forty days and forty nights he fled on foot, eating food provided along the way by an angel of God. When he arrived at the mountain where God had given the tablets of the law to Moses, Elijah went inside a cave to rest. Suddenly he heard a voice say, "What are you doing here, Elijah?"

"The people of Israel have forsaken your covenant," said Elijah, "and they seek my life, to take it away."

The voice said, "Go and stand upon the mountain before GOD."

As Elijah stood on the mountain, a great wind passed by, so great that the rocks broke before it. But Elijah knew that God was not in the wind. Then there was an earthquake, but God was not in the earthquake. And after the earthquake came fire, but God was not in the fire either. Then Elijah heard a still, small voice. "What are you doing here, Elijah?"

Elijah covered his face with his cloak, for he knew that the still, small voice was the voice of God.

"Go to the wilderness of Damascus and anoint Hazael to be king of Syria, and Jehu king over Israel. Elisha you shall anoint to be prophet in your place."

Elijah did as he was instructed, and then God told him to return to the city of Ahab and Jezebel for they had sinned again.

Near their palace, there was a vineyard which Ahab wanted very much, but it belonged to a man named Naboth and Naboth refused to sell it to the king. "GOD forbid that I should give you the inheritance of my fathers," Naboth said.

When Jezebel saw Ahab pouting around the palace she had Naboth falsely accused of blasphemy against God and treason against the king. And the elders of the village stoned him to death. Then she told Ahab, "Arise, take possession of the vineyard of Naboth, which he refused to give you for money. For Naboth is not alive, but dead."

When Ahab came into the vineyard, there stood Elijah with a message from God. "Thus says GOD: 'In the place where dogs licked up the blood of Naboth shall dogs lick up your blood.'"

"Have you found me, O my enemy?" asked Ahab.

"I have found you," said Elijah. "And of Jezebel, GOD also said, 'The dogs shall eat Jezebel within the bounds of Jezreel.'"

Both Ahab and Jezebel died as Elijah had predicted. Jehu, who was one of Ahab's captains and who would become Israel's next king, put to death Ahab's whole family and all those who worshiped Baal in Israel.

Finally, the time came for Elijah to pass his prophet's mantle to Elisha. "Ask what I shall do for you, before I am taken from you," he said to Elisha.

"Please," said Elisha, "let me inherit a double share of your spirit."

"You have asked a hard thing," Elijah said. "Yet if you see me as I am being taken from you, it shall be so for you. But if you do not see me, it shall not be so."

Suddenly, a chariot of fire, drawn by horses of fire, came between them and a whirlwind carried Elijah up to heaven.

"My father, my father!" Elisha cried. But Elijah was gone and no one in Israel ever saw him again. In the years to come, however, Elijah's return was awaited by the people of Israel as a signal that God had come once again to judge the nation. In the very last lines of the Hebrew scriptures, the prophet Malachi wrote: "I will send you Elijah the prophet before the great and terrible day of GOD comes. And Elijah will turn the hearts of parents to their children and the hearts of children to their parents, lest I come and smite the land with a curse." And every year, at the celebration of Passover—to this very day—the descendants of Judah leave one vacant chair in case Elijah should return.

In spite of some early attempts to purify Israel, after Elijah anointed him king, Jehu too sinned against God by offering sacrifices to the golden bulls at Bethel and at Dan. According to the biblical writers, for the next one hundred years, every king of the northern tribes of Israel sinned against God.

When Jeroboam the Second was king of Israel, there was one brief period of peace. But during that time the wealth of Israel was held by a few, while poverty was great throughout the land. A visitor from Judah named Amos saw the corruption of a northern marketplace, where people were bought and sold as slaves. Amos was not a prophet; he was a herdsman by trade, and "a dresser of sycamore trees." Yet he saw how the wicked merchants then attended religious festivals and made their small offerings to God. Amos spoke God's words to the people:

"I hate, I despise your feasts,
and I take no delight in your solemn assemblies.
Even though you offer me your burnt offerings and cereal offerings,
I will not accept them,
and the peace offerings of your fatted beasts
I will not look upon.
Take away from me the noise of your songs;
to the melody of your harps I will not listen.
But let justice roll down like waters,
and righteousness like an everflowing stream."

To Jeroboam, Amos said, "Jeroboam shall die by the sword, and Israel must go into exile away from his land." Amos was forced to leave Israel, but his prophecies eventually came true.

Assyria, the kingdom to the north beyond the river, had grown strong through the years that Israel grew weak. The Assyrian king, Sargon, destroyed the fortifications at Samaria. He took most of the Israelites away into exile and brought in other conquered captive peoples to work the land growing crops for the people of Assyria. These foreigners married Israelites who remained in the land. Their descendants became known as Samaritans. Because Samaritans were a mixed-race people and the southern Judahites, or Jews, were not, there was from that time on hatred between their peoples.

During this time of division, however, the people of the Southern Kingdom of Judah lived in relative peace. Judah's closeness to Egypt was often a problem as Egyptian rulers attempted to increase the size of their nation by decreasing the size of their neighbors' kingdom. One time, King Shishak of Egypt even raided the temple in Jerusalem and took away all of Solomon's treasures.

When Ahaz became king of Judah, he refused to side with Israel and neighboring Syria in an attempted war against Assyria. Instead he paid tribute—silver and gold from the temple treasury—to keep Assyrian soldiers away. Ahaz was very worried that even God would not be able to protect Judah from its enemies. A prophet named Isaiah assured Ahaz of God's care for Judah, however, saying, "Be quiet, do not fear. Ask a sign of the LORD your God."

"I will not put GOD to a test," replied Ahaz.

"Therefore GOD will give you a sign," said Isaiah. "A young woman shall conceive and bear a child whom she shall call Immanuel."

Immanuel means "God is with us," but Ahaz did not share Isaiah's trust. When Ahaz sent tribute money to Assyria, Judah became a subject nation. To raise the money, the heavily-taxed people of Judah had to be taxed even more. After Israel in the north fell to the Assyrians, Ahaz dismantled the altar of God in Jerusalem and built altars to the pagan gods of Assyria.

When Ahaz died, he was succeeded by his son, Hezekiah. The prophet Isaiah knew that Hezekiah would be a good king. It may even have been for Hezekiah's enthronement that Isaiah wrote:

> The people who walked in darkness
>   have seen a great light;
> those who dwelt in a land of deep darkness,
>   on them has light shined. . . .
> For to us a child is born,
>   to us an heir is given;
> . . . .
>   of peace there will be no end,
> upon the throne of David, and over his kingdom,
>   to establish it, and to uphold it
> with justice and with righteousness
>   from this time forth and forevermore.

Hezekiah decided to revolt against Assyria by not paying tribute, so Sennacherib, King of Assyria, headed toward Jerusalem with all his troops. On the way, Sennacherib defeated forty-six cities and took two hundred thousand people captive. In fear and trembling, then, Hezekiah consulted the prophet Isaiah who reassured him, saying, "Thus says GOD: 'The king of Assyria shall not come into this city, or shoot an arrow there. For I will defend this city to save it, for my own sake and for the sake of my servant David.'"

According to the biblical writer, that night an angel of God killed one hundred and eighty-five thousand Assyrian soldiers. Perhaps they were struck by a plague, or perhaps Sennacherib had to fight a battle somewhere else. The only thing the people of Judah knew was that in the morning, the Assyrian army was gone.

Sometime later, Hezekiah became so sick that he almost died. The king of Babylon, Merodachbaladan, sent messengers to him with a gift. Hezekiah showed the messengers all the wealth Judah had left—the silver, the gold, the spices, the precious oil, all that was in his storehouses and his whole armory.

When Isaiah heard of this, he said, "What did these men say? And from where did they come?"

"They have come to me from a far country, from Babylon," Hezekiah replied.

Isaiah was amazed that Hezekiah would show all his wealth to a foreign king, and said to him, "Hear the word of GOD: The days are coming, when all that is in your house, and all that which your fathers have stored up till this day, shall be carried to Babylon. Nothing shall be left, says GOD."

Hezekiah had no thought for the future, but only for his own generation. "The word of GOD which you have spoken is good," he said. "There will be peace and security in my days."

The time would come when even Judah would be taken into exile, for a land which had suffered such division could not stand. But even so, Isaiah, the prophet, had a vision that one day far into the future GOD would restore the people to their promised land:

> And there will be a highway from Assyria
>   for the remnant which is left of God's people,
> as there was for Israel
>   when they came up from the land of Egypt.

CHAPTER 8

EXILE

When King Hezekiah died, his son, Manasseh, at the age of twelve, came to the throne of Judah. He was far too young to know how to rule well and soon had reestablished pagan practices of worship throughout the land. When he grew up and had a son of his own, Manasseh offered his son up as a burnt sacrifice to his gods.

After Manasseh, another son Amon ruled for two years. Then Josiah, son of Amon, came to the throne at the age of eight. Josiah wanted to make up for the sins of the kings who had reigned before him, so in the eighteenth year of his reign, he set about restoring the temple in Jerusalem for the worship of God.

One day, the workers found a scroll in the temple which they brought in to the king. Josiah heard the words of the scroll and then tore his clothes in sorrow.

Then to Hilkiah the priest, he commanded, "Go, inquire of GOD for me, concerning the words of this book that has been found. For great is the wrath of GOD that is kindled against us, because our ancestors have not obeyed the words of this book."

The men took the scroll to the prophet Huldah, and she said, "Thus says GOD: 'I will bring evil upon this place and upon its inhabitants. Because they have forsaken me and have burned incense to other gods, my wrath will not be quenched.'"

Immediately, Josiah called the people to the temple and he read all the words of the book of the covenant which had been found in the house of God. Then they renewed the covenant with God which their ancestors had made when they were in the wilderness with Moses. All of the altars to Asherah and Baal were brought out of the temple and destroyed, and the altar at Bethel was crushed. The scroll, which may have been the book of Deuteronomy, not only gave instructions for purifying the worship of God, but it also described the way festivals were to be celebrated, including the Festival of Passover.

The biblical writers approved of Josiah: "Before him there was no king like him, who turned to the Lord with all his heart and soul and might, according to all the law of Moses, nor did any like him arise after him." Josiah ruled Judah well for thirty-one years, and even attempted to reunite Judah with Israel as it had been in the time of David, until events beyond Judah's borders changed everything.

Nineveh, the capital city of Assyria, fell to the powerful Babylonians. Then Egypt, under Pharaoh Neco, also grew in strength. Both countries looked at the land of Judah which lay between them. One day, Neco led his army into Judah to capture it for Egypt. Josiah called out the troops of Judah, but at Megiddo, on the plain of Esdraelon, he was mortally wounded by an Egyptian archer. All Judah mourned the loss of the one whom they had come to call "good king Josiah."

Pharaoh Neco put Josiah's son, Jehoikim, on the throne of Judah. Under Jehoikim's rule, the people again worshiped false gods. In the Valley of Hinnom, they even sacrificed their own children as burnt offerings. Then there arose a prophet named Jeremiah, who spoke for God: "Thus says GOD,

'I remember the devotion of your youth,
how you followed me in the wilderness.
I brought you into a plentiful land
  to enjoy its fruits and its good things.
But when you came in you defiled my land,
  and made my heritage an abomination.'"

Jeremiah told the people that the day would come when they would surrender and be taken as captives to Babylon. Unless they repented, he said, captivity in Babylon would be God's punishment for their sins. One day Jeremiah stood before the people at the gate to the temple and cried: "Amend your ways," says the LORD, "and I will let you dwell in this place. Do not trust in these deceptive words: 'This is the temple of GOD, the temple of GOD, the temple of GOD.' Will you steal, murder, burn incense to Baal, and then come and stand before me in this house, which is called by my name, and say, 'We are delivered!'—only to go on doing all these abominations? Has this house, which is called by my name, become a den of robbers?"

Because Jeremiah wept for his people, he came to be known as the weeping prophet. He wrote,

Is there no balm in Gilead?
Is there no physician there?
O that my head were waters,
and my eyes a fountain of tears,
that I might weep day and night.

When God first called Jeremiah to speak to the people, Jeremiah had protested: "I do not know how to speak, for I am only a youth." But God had said,

"Do not say, 'I am only a youth';
for to all to whom I send you, you shall go,
and whatever I command you, you shall speak.
I have put my words in your mouth."

The assurance that God was with him gave Jeremiah the courage to do many bold things. One day at a potter's house, Jeremiah bought a clay pot that had a crack in it. He took the pot to the Hinnom Valley and breaking it before the people, he cried, "Thus says the GOD of hosts: 'So will I break this people and this city, so that it can never be mended.'" Another time, Jeremiah buried a linen waistcloth by the banks of the Euphrates. When he dug it up, it was full of holes. He showed this to the people and said, "Thus says GOD: 'Even so will I spoil the pride of Judah and the pride of Jerusalem. This evil people shall be like this waistcloth, which is good for nothing.'" And again, when Zedekiah, the next king of Judah, was having a meeting with the kings of Edom, Moab, Ammon, Tyre, and Sidon to plan an uprising against Babylon, Jeremiah put an ox yoke around his shoulders to show them they must surrender to Babylon's might. He said, "Bring your necks under the yoke of the king of Babylon, and serve him and his people, and live. Why should this city become a desolation?"

When some of the leaders of Judah had been taken away into captivity in Babylon, Jeremiah wrote a letter to them: "Thus says the GOD of hosts, the God of Israel, to all the exiles whom I have sent into exile from Jerusalem to Babylon: Build houses and live in them; plant gardens and eat their produce. Take wives and husbands and have sons and daughters; multiply there, and do not decrease. When seventy years are completed for Babylon, I will visit you, and I will fulfill to you my promise and bring you back to this place."

One day, when Jeremiah was leaving the city on business, he was arrested and charged with desertion. Although he was now in prison, Jeremiah continued to urge the people to surrender. When the princes heard of this, they said to Zedekiah: "Let this man be put to death, for he is weakening the hands of the soldiers who are left in this city. This man is not seeking the welfare of this people, but their harm."

Zedekiah said to them, "He is in your hands."

So the princes cast Jeremiah into a deep well and left him there to die. Later that night, however, a palace servant named Ebed-melech (the name means "servant of the king") pulled Jeremiah out of the well. For his lifesaving rescue, Ebed-melech was promised safety during the coming invasion.

As Jeremiah had prophesied, King Nebuchadnezzar of Babylon attacked Jerusalem with his whole army. Nearly two years later, the Babylonians broke through the walls of Jerusalem. They destroyed the temple and burned down all the houses. Everything of gold, silver, or bronze they took back to Babylon.

Zedekiah and his court fled as far as the plains near Jericho before they were captured. The Babylonians killed Zedekiah's sons and put out Zedekiah's eyes; then the former king of Judah was led in chains to Babylon. Jeremiah remained in Jerusalem with the people who were not taken captive. One day, the people began to talk of fleeing to Egypt and they came to Jeremiah to ask him to pray for them. Jeremiah warned them. "Thus says the LORD of hosts, the God of Israel, 'As my anger and my wrath were poured out on the inhabitants of Jerusalem, so my wrath will be poured out on you when you go to Egypt.'"

'You are telling a lie!" shouted one of the men. And others began to accuse Jeremiah of betraying the people to the Babylonians.

The people packed what was left of their belongings and headed for Egypt. Although he knew they were doomed, Jeremiah went with them. Again and again his warnings went unheeded and tradition says that in Egypt the people stoned Jeremiah to death. Fortunately, a man named Baruch wrote Jeremiah's words in a journal so that future generations might know that Jeremiah was not always angry and depressed but he could be hopeful, too.

Baruch wrote, "'The days are coming,' says GOD, 'when I will make a new covenant with the house of Israel and the house of Judah, not like the covenant which I made with their ancestors when I took them by the hand to bring them out of the land of Egypt, my covenant which they broke. But this is the covenant which I will make with the house of Israel after those days. I will put my law within them, and I will write it upon their hearts; and I will be their God and they will be my people. They shall all know me, from the least of them to the greatest; for I will forgive their iniquity, and I will remember their sin no more.'"

In Babylon, meanwhile, the people who had been taken captive were remembering Jerusalem and they longed to go home. "Sing us one of the songs of Zion!" taunted their captors. The people's reply was recorded in Psalm 137:

By the waters of Babylon,
there we sat down and wept,
when we remembered Zion.

On the willows there
  we hung up our lyres.
For there our captors
  required of us songs,
and our tormentors, mirth, saying,
  "Sing us one of the songs of Zion!"
How shall we sing GOD'S song
  in a foreign land?
If I forget you, O Jerusalem,
  let my right hand wither!
Let my tongue cleave to the roof of my mouth,
  if I do not remember you,
if I do not set Jerusalem
  above my highest joy!

In Babylon the people sat down and wept. They also sat down and edited their scriptures. For centuries, the history of the people of faith had been handed down, one generation after another, through stories told by parents to their children and on scrolls written by people called scribes. Now, far away from the promised land, the people remembered God's promise and the hope they had of returning. They gathered their stories together into one series of scrolls that came to be known as the Hebrew scriptures. And they gathered themselves together into one place known as a synagogue (which means "gathered together") to study their scriptures. Because there was no temple in Babylon where their God could be worshiped, the synagogue became very important to the people.

Often they would ask one another how such a disaster could have befallen them and why God did not save even the temple from destruction. A priest named Ezekiel, who had already spent a decade in exile, told the people that before the temple was destroyed, he had prayed that God would defend it.

"The guilt of the house of Israel and Judah is exceedingly great," Ezekiel heard God reply. "The city is full of injustice. I will requite their deeds upon their heads."

Ezekiel told the people that God had appointed him to be a watcher for the house of Israel and that God had also given him a vision of a valley of dry bones. The bones were the scattered and lifeless people of Israel, but when God's spirit was breathed upon them, the bones rose up and lived again. The people of Israel, Ezekiel said, were a people without a shepherd, but the day would come when God would find a shepherd for them.

"Thus says the Lord GOD," reported Ezekiel, "as a shepherd seeks out his flock when some of the sheep have been scattered abroad, so I will seek out my sheep. I will gather them from the countries, and will bring them into their own land. And I will set up over them one shepherd, my servant David; he shall feed them and be their shepherd. And I will make with them a covenant of peace."

While they were in exile, the people of Judah (who were now and ever after known as "Jews") tried hard to obey the laws of their faith, believing that, if only they were obedient to all the laws, God would restore them to their homeland. One of the psalmists wrote:

Your word is a lamp to my feet
  and a light to my path.
Let me live, that I might praise you,
  and let your ordinances help me.
I have gone astray like a lost sheep; seek your servant,
  for I do not forget your commandments.

There was another prophet who also loved God and the people. His name is no longer known, but his writings became part of the book of Isaiah. This prophet believed that those who followed God should expect to suffer and that Israel in captivity was God's "suffering servant." He wrote that God says:

"It is too light a thing that you should be my servant
  to raise up the tribes of Jacob
  and to restore the preserved of Israel;
I will give you as a light to the nations,
  that my salvation may reach to the end of the earth."

This prophet also believed that the people had been scattered like sheep:

All we like sheep have gone astray;
  we have turned everyone to our own way;
and GOD has laid on this one
  the iniquity of us all.

But the prophet believed that even though the people were in exile, God had plans to set them free. Isaiah, chapter 40, one of the greatest chapters in the Bible, describes the prophet's vision of Israel's future and freedom, beginning with these words:

Comfort, comfort my people,
  says your god,
Speak tenderly to Jerusalem,
  and cry to it
that its warfare is ended,
  that its iniquity is pardoned,
that it has received from GOD'S hand
  double for all its sins.

A voice cries:
"In the wilderness prepare the way of GOD,
make straight in the desert a highway for our God."

When Cyrus of Persia began to conquer land held by Babylon, the Jews began to hope that Cyrus might be the one God had anointed to set them free. The prophet wrote:

Thus says GOD to God's anointed, to Cyrus,
"For the sake of my servant Jacob,
and Israel my chosen,
I call you by your name."

When Cyrus came into the city of Babylon, the Babylonians surrendered without even a skirmish. When he had established Persian rule in the land, Cyrus wrote this command: "Thus says Cyrus, king of Persia: 'The LORD, the God of heaven, has given me all the kingdoms of the earth, and God has charged me to build God a house at Jerusalem, which is in Judah. Whoever is among you of all God's people, may their God be with them. Let them go up to Jerusalem.'"

Thus it was that after a captivity which had lasted seventy years, the Jews were allowed to return to Israel. All did not return, of course, for in those years some had acquired land and homes and a way of life they enjoyed. Many had been born in Babylon and to them Babylon was their native land. But according to the scriptures, forty-two thousand did return and when they returned, they set about repairing the temple that lay in ruins in a barren and wasted land.

But the resettlement of Israel was not easy. First, the people who had moved into the land while the Jews were away resisted their return. They attacked those who worked on the temple until the discouraged Jews gave it up to concentrate on their own houses and farms. At last, under the leadership of Zerubbabel, the people rebuilt God's temple. As soon as the temple foundations were laid, the people again began to worship God on Mt. Zion, the "mountain of God," as their ancestors had done.

Almost a century went by and still the wall around Jerusalem lay in ruins. But then from Babylon there came two Jews who would restore both the wall and the word of God.

One was Nehemiah, an official in the Persian court. When he heard that the wall was still in ruins, Nehemiah wept. The king of Persia, seeing Nehemiah's grief, gave him permission to travel to Judah, which by now was called Judea, to repair the wall. However, repairing the wall was no easier a task than was rebuilding the temple. Because Nehemiah had to contend with neighboring enemies who tried to tear the wall down, he ordered the workers to carry tools in one hand and weapons in the other. While half the men worked, the other half stood guard. After fifty-two days the wall was completed, and the people gathered to celebrate. Songs were sung and prayers were lifted up to God. Then Ezra, a second Jew from Babylon and a scribe, stood at one of the gates and read the law to the people. When the people heard what the law required, they wept in sorrow for their sins. Then they celebrated the Feast of Booths to remember the years their ancestors had spent in the wilderness.

From the time of Ezra and the return of the law, and of Nehemiah and the rebuilding of the temple and the wall, the people were a nation with God at the center of all things. Their laws were religious, their festivals were religious, and they chose their friends and families for reasons that were largely religious.

Although the people longed for a king of their own to rule again in Judea, from the eighth century before the birth of Jesus to the twentieth century of our own time, the land of Israel would remain under foreign rule.

After the Babylonians and Persians, the Greeks controlled the land. And after the Greeks, the Romans conquered all the known world.

When the land was held by the Greeks, there arose a group of Jews who approved of Greek ways; they came to be known as Sadducees. A second group clung closely to Jewish law and customs; they came to be known as Pharisees.

The people continued to tell stories that would help them to understand why their lives were so hard. One story told of Daniel, a Jew in Persia, who had been put through many hard trials for his faith. Another told of Esther, a young Jewish woman who had saved her people from persecution. A third story was about a righteous man named Job who had suffered unbelievable diseases and sorrow, and yet remained faithful to God.

Then one day someone told a different type of story, a story that told of the way God loved all people, not only a chosen few. Jonah was the hero of the story, and, against Jonah's will, God told him to prophesy even to Assyrians, the people of Nineveh. Jonah did not want to go to Nineveh. In fact, he sailed away on a ship headed in the opposite direction. But God appointed a great fish to put Jonah back on course again. When Jonah did as God commanded and prophesied even to foreigners, they repented of their sins and, like the Jews, they were saved.

You shall be "a light to the nations," Isaiah had said.

The exile was over and the day was coming when that promise from the prophets would come true.

CHAPTER 9

PROMISE

"Repent, for the kingdom of heaven is at hand."

Crowds had gathered beside the Jordan River to hear John the Baptist preach and to see him baptize those who repented of their sins. John had told them that he was the one Isaiah had written of so long ago:

> "The voice of one crying in the wilderness:
> Prepare the way of the Sovereign,
> make the paths of the Sovereign straight."

John wore a garment of camel's hair and a belt made of hide. People said that he ate locusts and wild honey and some even said that he must be Elijah the prophet who had come back at last to usher in the day of the Sovereign. Others thought John was the Christ (Christ is a Greek word, and like the Hebrew word messiah, it means "anointed"). The Jews were hoping that God had finally anointed someone to rescue them from the oppression they were suffering as an occupied territory of Rome.

Not that there were not some good things to be said about Roman occupation. New roads connected all parts of the country. Aqueducts brought water to a land which had once been thorns and thistles and dry as the dust. And Roman soldiers, visible everywhere, assured that the Roman pax, or peace, would be kept no matter what.

But there were many more bad things to be said about Rome. Roman taxes were so high that many Jewish people lived in poverty; some even had to sell themselves or their children as slaves. There was none of the promised freedom to sit under their own "vine and fig tree." The Jews had been given permission to worship God in the new temple in Jerusalem which King Herod had built—again from the people's taxes—but their religious leaders were ever-cautious that nothing new be taught which might threaten the Jews' fragile relationship with Rome.

John and his followers were watched very closely. It had been over four hundred years since Ezra had stood near the temple gate reading the law and reminding the people of their sins. When the Pharisees—those who taught the law—and the Sadducees—those who led worship in the temple—came to John for repentance, he shouted, "You brood of vipers! Who warned you to flee from the wrath to come?"

But to his followers, John said, "I baptize you with water for repentance, but the one who is coming after me is mightier than I, whose sandals I am not worthy to carry; that one will baptize you with the Holy Spirit and with fire."

One day, Jesus of Nazareth came from Galilee to be baptized by John in the Jordan. Jesus was John's cousin and yet John exclaimed, "I need to be baptized by you, and do you come to me?"

"Let it be so now," Jesus answered him, "for thus it is fitting to fulfill all righteousness."

So John baptized Jesus. And when Jesus came up out of the water, he looked up and saw the heavens open and the Holy Spirit in the form of a dove descending on him. Then a voice from heaven said, "This is my beloved Child, with whom I am well pleased."

In later years, sometime after Jesus had died, the writers of the Gospels, or accounts of the "good news" Jesus preached, searched for ways to describe Jesus to those who had never met him.

The one who wrote the Gospel of John described Jesus as the Word of God "made flesh." Jesus existed with God from the beginning of the world, he wrote, when God created all things with the Word. "Let there be light," God had said—then there was light. And now, in Jesus, God again sent light to shine in the midst of human sin and despair. It was because of his belief that Jesus had existed "in the beginning" that the author of John did not include information in his Gospel about Jesus' earthly birth.

The one who wrote the Gospel of Mark may have known only of Jesus' adult ministry for, like John, he, too, mentioned nothing about Jesus' birth. But the writers of the Gospels of Matthew and Luke both included stories of Jesus' birth. The two stories were very different and expressed two very different hopes the people had for the promised one of God.

In Luke's Gospel, the story was told of an angel named Gabriel who visited Mary of Nazareth. Gabriel's message to Mary is called an annunciation and is similar to the annunciation of other births in the Bible (such as the births of Ishmael and Samson).

"Do not be afraid, Mary, for you have found favor with God. You will conceive in your womb and bear a child, whose name you shall call Jesus.

This one will be great, and will be called the Child of the Most High;
and the Lord God will give to that Child the throne of David, the ancestor of the Child,
to reign over the house of Jacob forever;
and of that reign there will be no end."

"I am the servant of God," Mary told the angel. "Let it be to me according to your word."

Shortly after the angel's annunciation, Mary sang a song, very much like the one Hannah had sung, centuries earlier, when she became the mother of Samuel, the prophet who had anointed King David.

"My soul magnifies the Lord,
and my spirit rejoices in God my Savior, . . .
God has shown strength with God's arm,
has scattered the proud in the imagination of their hearts,
God has put down the mighty from their thrones,
and exalted those of low degree."

When a decree went out that all the Roman world should be enrolled, Mary and her betrothed husband, Joseph, traveled from Nazareth to Bethlehem. Joseph was a descendant of King David and needed to return to the place of his ancestor's birth for the census.

Because the town was crowded, Mary and Joseph spent the night in a stable and it was there that Jesus was born.

In the hills surrounding Bethlehem, a small band of shepherds guarded their sheep, as David himself had done long before. Suddenly, an angel appeared to the shepherds with good news: "Be not afraid; for I bring you good news of a great joy which will come to all the people; for to you is born this day in the city of David a Savior who is Christ the Sovereign."

Then the shepherds saw more angels and heard them sing:

"Glory to God in the highest!
And on earth peace."

The shepherds hurried to the stable, and when they saw the baby Jesus in the manger, they returned to their sheep, praising God.

By including this story of Jesus' birth in his Gospel, Luke remembered the promise in the Hebrew scriptures that a shepherd-king like David would one day come again to rule the Kingdom of Judah.

Would Jesus, "Son of David," fulfill the promise? Luke wondered. Would he be a shepherd-king?

On the other hand, according to Matthew it was not Mary who received word of Jesus' birth; it was Joseph. Joseph did not see an angel, but heard one speak to him in a dream, like that other dreamer, Joseph, son of Jacob. Long ago, the first Joseph-the-dreamer had saved his father and eleven brothers from starvation by helping them escape into Egypt during a famine. Joseph, the husband of Mary, would soon save his family in the same way.

In Matthew's Gospel it was not shepherds who came to visit Jesus, but Magi, rulers from the East. They followed a star to the place where the child was. (They may have heard of the promise in the book of Numbers: "A star shall come forth out of Jacob.")

The Magi arrived in Judea, asking, "Where is the one who has been born king of the Jews?" When King Herod heard their question, he summoned the Magi to his palace, saying, "Go and search diligently for the child, and when you have found him bring me word, that I too may come and worship him."

The Magi found Jesus in Bethlehem; they bowed before him, presenting gifts of gold, frankincense, and myrrh. They did not return to Herod, however, because they were warned in a dream to depart by another road.

When word reached Herod that Jesus had been born, he ordered all the male babies in Bethlehem two years old and under to be killed. But Joseph, dreaming again, was told to escape into Egypt with Mary and the child. In this way, the prophecy of Hosea would be fulfilled: "Out of Egypt I called my child."

In time, Mary and Joseph and Jesus came out of Egypt and went to live in Galilee where one day Jesus would begin his ministry of liberation.

By including this story of Jesus' birth in his Gospel, Matthew remembered Joseph-the-dreamer who had saved the sons of Jacob by leading them into Egypt. And he remembered Moses, the baby who survived death at the hand of the Egyptian pharaoh, and grew up to return his people to freedom in a land of their own.

Matthew wondered: Would Jesus, descendant of Joseph-the-dreamer, fulfill the promise? Like Moses, would he set the people free?

Thus, from the very beginning of their Gospels, those who wrote of Jesus' life knew that he would be a sovereign ruler and shepherd of the people like David, a liberator of the oppressed like Moses, and even God's Word made flesh. And that is what was confirmed at Jesus' baptism: that, more than anything else, he was the Child of God.

Jesus, filled with the Spirit, went into the wilderness to fast and pray and to consider what form his ministry might take. Moses had spent forty days on the mountain in the wilderness receiving the tablets of God's law. Jesus stayed in the wilderness for forty days remembering those laws and dedicating himself to obeying them and to serving God. There, according to the Gospel writers, Jesus was tempted by the devil to use God's power for Jesus' own glory. But each time the devil tempted him, Jesus overcame the temptation by remembering one of the laws of Moses.

The devil tempted Jesus: Could Jesus turn stones into bread and feed all the hungry of the world? Jesus, quoting the Hebrew scriptures, replied:

> "One shall not live by bread alone,
> but by every word that proceeds from the mouth of God."

Again the devil tempted Jesus: Should Jesus overturn God's laws of nature; could he jump from a tower and not die?

"You shall not tempt the Lord your God," quoted Jesus.

A third time the devil tempted Jesus: Should Jesus worship the false idols of the earth and gain wealth and power for himself? Again, Jesus quoted,

> "You shall worship the Lord your God
> and God only shall you serve."

After the forty days were over, Jesus returned to Galilee and began his ministry. And the power of the Holy Spirit was with him.

When Jesus returned to his hometown of Nazareth, he went to the synagogue and stood up to read the scriptures to the congregation. He opened the scrolls to the words of Isaiah and read:

> "The Spirit of God is upon me,
> because God has anointed me to preach good news to the poor,
> and has sent me to proclaim release to the captives
> and recovering of sight to those who are blind,
> to set at liberty those who are oppressed,
> to proclaim the acceptable year of the Sovereign."

When Jesus finished his reading, the people stared expectantly at him, for this passage described what their Messiah would do when he came to rescue Israel from its captors. Was Jesus the one who would "set at liberty those who were oppressed?"

Then Jesus spoke. "Today," he announced, "this scripture has been fulfilled in your hearing." The people were amazed, and all spoke well of him and of the things he said.

"Is not this Joseph's son?" someone asked. Nazareth was a small town and the people had known Jesus for thirty years. It must have surprised them to hear his sudden announcement that he was anointed by God. They wanted to hear more, but what Jesus said next was not what they wanted to hear.

"I tell you, there were many widows in Israel in the days of Elijah, when there came a great famine over all the land. And Elijah was sent to none of them but only to Zarephath, in the land of Sidon, to a woman who was a widow. And there were many people with leprosy in Israel in the time of the prophet Elisha; and none of them was cleansed, but only Naaman, the Syrian."

Jesus reminded the people that Elijah, that great prophet whose return they awaited, and his follower, Elisha, had ministered not to their own people but to foreigners. The Jews of Nazareth were awaiting a messiah who would liberate the Jews—their own people—not foreigners, and certainly not Romans. If Isaiah's promise had been fulfilled in their hearing, and if the promise included good news, recovery of sight, and liberty to foreigners, the people of Nazareth wanted nothing to do with it.

A furious mob seized Jesus and took him to a hill outside of town. They began to push him toward the edge of the hill so he would fall down and die. But Jesus passed through the crowd and walked away, leaving Nazareth forever.

As it turned out, God's promise had been fulfilled in the people's hearing. In Jesus, God's Word became flesh and the people of Judah—and the people of all nations—would soon know liberation as they had known it with Moses. And, like David, Jesus would be a good shepherd, one who would even lay down his life for his sheep. When Jesus was nailed to the cross, a sign was put up over his head: "This is Jesus of Nazareth, King of the Jews." From that day to this, the name Jesus would always be linked with the name of the city that rejected him.

For Jesus had come—and the promise would be fulfilled—even for them.

CHAPTER 10

OBEDIENCE

Jesus left Nazareth and went down to Capernaum, a fishing village by the Sea of Galilee. When he saw two brothers, Simon who is called Peter, and Andrew, casting their nets into the sea, Jesus called to them: "Follow me, and I will make you fishers of women and men." They followed him along the shore until they came upon two more brothers, James and John, who were mending their nets. When Jesus called them, they also left their nets and followed him.

On the sabbath, Jesus taught at the synagogue and when he healed a man with an unclean spirit, people began to take notice of him.

"What is this?" they asked. "A new teaching! With authority Jesus commands even the unclean spirits, and they obey him."

Word began to spread throughout Capernaum, and at sundown, when the sabbath had ended, people brought all those who were sick to Jesus' home and he healed them.

Soon, Jesus and his followers were going about Galilee, teaching in synagogues and preaching the gospel and healing every disease. And great crowds gathered around him—from Galilee, the Decapolis, Jerusalem, Judea, and beyond the Jordan River. And Jesus' followers began to write down some of his sayings. One group of sayings is called the Sermon on the Mount. It begins with a series of blessings, or Beatitudes:

> "Blessed are the poor in spirit, for theirs is the kingdom of heaven.
> "Blessed are those who mourn, for they shall be comforted.
> "Blessed are the meek, for they shall inherit the earth.
> "Blessed are those who hunger and thirst for righteousness, for they shall be satisfied.

"Blessed are the merciful, for they shall obtain mercy.
"Blessed are the pure in heart, for they shall see God.
"Blessed are the peacemakers, for they shall be called children of God.
"Blessed are those who are persecuted for righteousness' sake, for theirs is the kingdom of heaven.
"Blessed are you when others revile you and persecute you and utter all kinds of evil against you falsely on my account. Rejoice and be glad, for your reward is great in heaven, for so they persecuted the prophets who were before you."

"You are the salt of the earth," Jesus said, "but if salt has lost its taste, how shall its saltness be restored?

"You are the light of the world. A city set on a hill cannot be hid. No one lights a lamp and puts it under a bushel, but on a stand, and it gives light to all in the house. Let your light so shine before others, that they may see your good works and give glory to God who is in heaven."

Some of Jesus' sayings were shocking, like this one:

"You have heard that it was said, 'You shall love your neighbor and hate your enemy.' But I say to you, love your enemies and pray for those who persecute you. If you love those who love you, what credit is that to you? For even sinners love those who love them."

The people of Jesus' time worshiped God in three ways: by giving alms, or charity; by fasting; and by prayer. Here is what Jesus taught about these three "pillars of the faith." "When you give alms, sound no trumpet before you. Do not let your left hand know what your right hand is doing, so that your alms may be in secret. And when you fast, do not look dismal. Wash your face, that your fasting may not be seen by others. When you pray, go into your room and shut the door and pray to God who is in secret; and God who sees in secret will reward you."

Then Jesus told a story to encourage people to live by his teachings: "Everyone who hears these words of mine and does them will be like a wise person who built a house upon the rock; and the rain fell, and the floods came, and the winds blew and beat upon that house, but it did not fall, because it had been founded on the rock. And everyone who hears these words of mine and does not do them will be like the fool who built a house upon the sand; and the rain fell, and the floods came, and the winds blew and beat against that house, and it fell; and great was the fall of it."

When Jesus had finished his teachings, a man with leprosy approached him, stretched out his hand and said, "Lord, if you will, you can make me clean."

Jesus touched him, saying, "I will; be clean." And just then, the man's leprosy went away.

Sometime later, Jesus was surrounded by a great crowd, so he got in a boat to cross to the other shore. Suddenly there was a great wind and the boat was in danger of being swamped in the waves. Jesus, however, had fallen asleep in the stern.

"Save us, Lord; we are perishing!" called the disciples.

Jesus awoke and asked, "Why are you afraid, O men of little faith?" Then he rebuked the winds and the sea and there was a great calm.

"What sort of man is this," marveled the disciples, "that even winds and sea obey him?"

Jesus returned to Capernaum, and crowds once again filled his home to hear his teachings about the realm of God. When four men brought their paralyzed friend to Jesus for healing, they could not even get in the door. So they climbed up on the roof, removed the tiles, and lowered their friend's bed through the hole they had made. Jesus looked up, saw their faith, and said to the one who was paralyzed, "My child, your sins are forgiven."

The scribes and Pharisees who were gathered there were shocked by what Jesus said. "Who is this that speaks blasphemies?" they asked. "Who can forgive sins but God only?"

But Jesus said to them, "Why do you think evil in your hearts? For which is easier—to say, 'Your sins are forgiven,' or to say, 'Rise and walk'? That you may know that the Son of man has authority on earth to forgive sins,"—he then said to the one who was paralyzed—"Rise, take your bed and go home." And the person rose and went home.

Another day after Jesus had been teaching, one of the rulers of the synagogue approached and said, "My little daughter is at the point of death. Come and lay your hands on her, so that she may be made well, and live."

As usual, a great crowd followed them and in the crowd was a woman who had had a flow of blood for twelve years. She had spent all her money on physicians, but no one had been able to cure her disease. In fact, she felt even worse. She came up behind Jesus in the crowd and touched his garment.

"If I touch even his garments," she said to herself, "I shall be made well."

As she touched him, Jesus could feel his power go forth. He turned and said, "Who touched my garments?"

The woman in fear and trembling—and joy in her cure—fell at his feet and told him what she had done.

"Daughter," said Jesus, "your faith has made you well. Go in peace and be healed of your disease."

As she left, people came forth from the ruler's house, saying, "Your daughter is dead. Why trouble the Teacher any further?"

But Jesus said to the ruler, "Do not fear, only believe." Then he said to the mourners who had gathered there, "Why all this confusion and weeping? The child is not dead but sleeping."

They laughed at him, but Jesus took the little girl's hand and said in his native Aramaic, "Talitha cumi," which means "Little girl, I say to you, arise." And she did.

As Jesus went on from there, two men who were blind followed him and cried out, "Have mercy on us, Son of David."

Jesus said, "Do you believe that I am able to do this?"

"Yes, Lord," they replied.

Then Jesus touched their eyes, saying, "According to your faith be it done to you." And their eyes were opened. Jesus did not want them to tell anyone, but they spread his fame throughout the district.

As the men were going away, a demoniac, without speech, was brought to Jesus who cast out the demon. Then the man was able to speak again and the people said, "Never was anything like this seen in Israel."

Because there were so many people who needed help, Jesus called twelve disciples, giving them authority to cast out unclean spirits, and to heal disease; and then sent them out to teach and preach. They were: Simon Peter, Andrew, James, John, Philip, Bartholomew, Thomas, Matthew, James, the son of Alphaeus, Thaddaeus, Simon the Cananaean, and Judas Iscariot, who would betray him.

"Preach as you go, saying, 'The kingdom of heaven is at hand,'" Jesus told them. But he also warned them that troubles would come: "Whoever does not bear their own cross and come after me, cannot be my disciple."

As his fame spread, Jesus knew that soon the rulers would have to deal with him. His cousin John, already in prison, had sent him a message: "Are you the one who is to come, or shall we look for another?"

Jesus responded, "Go and tell John what you hear and see: those who are blind receive their sight and those who are lame walk, people with leprosy are cleansed and those who are deaf hear, and the dead are raised up, and those who are poor have good news preached to them."

John must have rejoiced at the news (even as he had leaped in his mother's womb when she received the visit of Mary). But his joy would not last, for soon John would die a martyr's death.

Some rulers, however, approved of Jesus' teachings. A Pharisee named Nicodemus came to him by night, saying, "Rabbi, we know that you are a teacher from God; for no one can do the signs that you do, except by the power of God."

Jesus told him, "Truly, truly, I say to you, unless one is born anew, one cannot see the realm of God."

"How can someone be born who is old?" asked Nicodemus. "Can anyone enter their mother's womb a second time and be born?"

Jesus' reply was very strange: "Unless one is born of water and the Spirit, one cannot enter the realm of God."

One day, Jesus—like Elijah—passed through Samaria. It was noon, the sixth hour, and Jesus, hot and thirsty, sat down beside a well. When a woman approached, Jesus said, "Give me a drink."

The woman was surprised. "How is it that you, a Jew, ask a drink of me, a woman of Samaria?"

"If you knew the gift of God, and who it is that is saying to you, 'Give me a drink,' you would have asked that person, who would then have given you living water. Whoever drinks of the water that I shall give will never thirst."

The woman agreed. "Sir, give me this water."

"Go, call your husband, and come here," Jesus said.

"I have no husband," she replied.

"You are right, for you have had five husbands, and he whom you now have is not your husband."

The woman must have been impressed by Jesus' knowledge, for she said, "Sir, I perceive you are a prophet. I know that Messiah is coming (the one who is called Christ), who will show us all things."

"I who speak to you am that very one," Jesus said.

At that, the woman ran back to her village and told them the good news. When the people saw Jesus, they asked him to stay with them and he stayed two days. "We have heard for ourselves," they rejoiced, "and we know this is indeed the Savior of the world."

There was another Pharisee named Simon who decided to test Jesus, so he invited him to dinner. While they were at table, a woman who was a sinner came up behind Jesus with an alabaster flask of ointment and she began to anoint his feet.

"If this man were a prophet," thought Simon, "he would have known who and what sort of woman this is who is touching him, for she is a sinner."

But Jesus said, "Simon, I have something to say to you. A certain creditor had two debtors; one owed five hundred denarii, and the other fifty. When they could not pay, the creditor forgave them both. Now which of them will love the creditor more?"

Simon replied, "The one, I suppose, to whom the creditor forgave more."

And Jesus said to Simon, "You have judged rightly. Do you see this woman? I entered your house, you gave me no water for my feet, but she has wet my feet with her tears and wiped them with her hair. You gave me no kiss, but from the time I came in she has not ceased to kiss my feet. You did not anoint my head with oil, but she has anointed my feet with ointment. Therefore I tell you, her sins, which are many, are forgiven, for she loved much; but whoever is forgiven little, loves little." Then Jesus turned to the woman and said, "Your sins are forgiven. Go in peace."

Jesus and the twelve disciples continued to preach in villages and towns and they were joined by many others: Mary, called Magdalene, from whom seven demons had gone out, and Joanna and Susanna and other women who gave money to the ministry and who followed all the way from Galilee to Jerusalem.

In addition to teachings, healings, and the casting out of demons, Jesus loved to tell stories, particularly stories called "parables." Parables were short stories or sayings that had secret meanings only the followers of Jesus could understand.

"To you it has been given to know the secrets of the kingdom of heaven," said Jesus, "but for those outside everything is in parables. Blessed are your eyes, for they see, and your ears, for they hear."

Here is one of Jesus' parables:

"A sower went out to sow. And as the seeds were being scattered, some seeds fell along the path, and the birds came and devoured them. Other seeds fell on rocky ground, where they had not much soil, and immediately they sprang up, since they had no depth of soil, but when the sun rose they were scorched; and since they had no root they withered away. Other seeds fell upon thorns, and the thorns grew up and choked them. Other seeds fell on good soil and brought forth grain, some a hundredfold, some sixty, some thirty."

The disciples had trouble understanding this parable, so Jesus explained it to them: "When any hear the word of the kingdom and do not understand it, the evil one comes and snatches away what is sown in the heart; this is what was sown along the path. As for what was sown on rocky ground, this is the one who hears the word and immediately receives it with joy; yet having no root within, this one endures for awhile, and when tribulation or persecution arises on account of the word, immediately falls away. As for what was sown among thorns, this is the one who hears the word, but the cares of the world and the delight in riches choke the word, and it proves unfruitful. As for what was sown on good soil, this is the one who hears the word and understands it, who indeed bears fruit, and yields, in one case a hundredfold, in another sixty, and in another thirty."

Other parables went like this:

"The kingdom of heaven is like a grain of mustard seed which a man took and sowed in his field; it is the smallest of all seeds, but when it has grown it is the greatest of shrubs and becomes a tree, so that the birds of the air come and make nest in its branches."

"The kingdom of heaven is like leaven which a woman took and hid in three measures of flour, till it was all leavened."

"The kingdom of heaven is like treasure hidden in a field, which someone found and covered up; then in great joy the finder goes and sells everything and buys that field."

"Again, the kingdom of heaven is like a merchant in search of fine pearls, who, on finding one pearl of great value, went and sold everything and bought it."

The disciples must have liked Jesus' parables, for they wrote many of them down. And sometimes it seemed as if the things Jesus did were parables, too—that is, they were happenings with great meanings. Like the time he and the disciples had gone away to a lonely place to rest awhile. They took a boat, but the people ran on ahead of them. When Jesus went ashore, he had compassion on the people for they seemed like sheep without a shepherd. Jesus taught them until late in the day and then the disciples said to him, "The hour is now late; send them away to go into the country and villages round about and buy themselves something to eat."

"You give them something to eat," said Jesus.

"Shall we go and buy two hundred denarii worth of bread, and give it to them to eat?" laughed the disciples.

"How many loaves have you? Go and see."

"Five, and two fish."

Commanding the people to sit in groups of one hundred and groups of fifty, Jesus took the five loaves and two fish, looked up to heaven, blessed, and broke the loaves and gave them to the disciples to set before the people. Then he divided the two fish among them all. Five thousand men and women and children ate that day. And the disciples took up what was left over—twelve baskets of broken pieces.

On another occasion, Jesus withdrew from a crowd and entered a house in the region of Tyre—Gentile country. A Gentile woman came to him and said, "My daughter is severely possessed by a demon."

The disciples were upset to see a Gentile woman talking with Jesus. "Send her away," they said, "for she is crying after us."

"I was sent only to the lost sheep of the house of Israel," Jesus told her. "It is not fair to take the children's bread and throw it to the dogs."

"Yes, Lord, yet even the dogs eat the crumbs that fall from their owners' table."

Jesus, who had fed five thousand people with five loaves, was impressed with her answer. "O woman, great is your faith! Be it done for you as you desire." When the woman got home, she found the child lying in bed and the demon gone.

One of the Gospel writers, like a disciple suddenly understanding the meaning of Jesus' parables, wrote that Jesus also said at the feeding of the five thousand, "I am the bread of life." The Gentile woman had found that to be true.

One day, Jesus asked the disciples: "Who do people say that I am?"

They said, "Some say John the Baptist, others say Elijah, and others Jeremiah or one of the prophets."

"But who do you say that I am?" he asked.

Peter confessed: "You are the Christ."

"Blessed are you, Simon!" said Jesus. "I tell you, you are Peter, and on this rock I will build my church." Though the disciples must have rejoiced at this news, they were suddenly shocked by what followed it, for now Jesus told them that he must go to Jerusalem to suffer, to be killed, and after three days, to rise again.

Peter cried: "God forbid, Lord! this shall never happen to you."

But Jesus did not want his disciples to try to stop him. "Get behind me, Satan! For you are not siding with God, but with humankind." And then he told them that being his disciples might even cost them their own lives.

"If any would come after me, let them deny themselves and take up their cross and follow me. For those who would save their life will lose it, and those who lose their life for my sake will find it."

Six days later, Jesus took Peter and James and John and went up a high mountain to pray. Suddenly Jesus was transfigured before them, his face shone as bright as the sun and his robe became white as light. Then the disciples saw two men talking with Jesus: Moses, representing the law, and Elijah, repesenting the prophets.

Peter was thrilled. "Lord, it is well that we are here. If you wish, I will make three booths here, one for you and one for Moses and one for Elijah."

But while Peter was speaking, a cloud overshadowed them and a voice spoke from the cloud: "This is my beloved Child with whom I am well pleased," said the voice, speaking the same words Jesus heard at his baptism. And then the voice added, "To this one you shall listen."

Hearing this, the disciples fell on their faces and were filled with awe. Jesus touched them and said, "Rise, and have no fear." And when they lifted up their eyes, they saw no one but Jesus only.

As Abraham had obeyed God by offering up as a sacrifice his only son, Isaac, so now Jesus would obey God by offering his own life as sacrifice for others. Jesus set his face to go to Jerusalem. And his disciples followed him.

CHAPTER 11

BLESSING

As the disciples learned more about God's realm, they began to wonder who would be the greatest there. James and John, thinking they deserved the honor, said to Jesus, "Grant us to sit, one at your right hand and one at your left, in your glory."

But Jesus told them, "You do not know what you are asking. Are you able to drink the cup that I drink?" (Jesus was asking if they were ready—as he was—to suffer and die for the realm of God.)

"We are able," they replied.

"You will drink my cup," Jesus agreed, knowing that his disciples would come to hard times, "but to sit at my right hand or at my left is not mine to grant."

When children were brought to Jesus that he might lay hands on them and bless them, the disciples tried to prevent the people from bothering him. But Jesus said, "Let the children come to me, and do not hinder them; for to such belongs the kingdom of heaven." And taking the children in his arms, Jesus blessed them.

One day some Pharisees and scribes saw Jesus eating with the tax collectors and sinners. They criticized Jesus, saying, "This man receives sinners and eats with them." And Jesus told some more parables.

"What man of you," he asked, "having a hundred sheep, if he has lost one of them, does not leave the ninety-nine in the wilderness, and go after the one which is lost, until he finds it? And when he has found it, lay it on his shoulders, rejoicing. And when he has come home, gather together his friends and his neighbors, saying to them, 'Rejoice with me, for I have found my sheep which was lost.' Just so, I tell you, there will be more joy in heaven over one sinner who repents than over ninety-nine righteous persons who need no repentance.

"Or what woman, having ten silver coins, if she loses one coin, does not light a lamp and sweep the house and seek diligently until she finds it? And when she has found it, call together her friends and neighbors, saying, 'Rejoice with me, for I have found the coin which I have lost.' Just so, I tell you, there is joy before the angels of God over one sinner who repents."

There was yet another parable which Jesus told about people who thought God favored them more than others:

"Two people went up into the temple to pray, one a Pharisee and the other a tax collector. The Pharisee stood and prayed thus, 'God, I thank you that I am not like other people, extortioners, unjust, adulterers, or even like this tax collector. I fast twice a week, I give tithes of all that I get.' But the tax collector, standing far off, would not even look up to heaven, but beat his breast, saying, 'God, be merciful to me a sinner!' I tell you, this one went home justified rather than the other; for all who exalt themselves will be humbled, but those who humble themselves will be exalted."

Jesus' parables were remembered by those who heard them, for they seemed so true to life. Perhaps the idea for the parable about the Pharisee and the tax collector came to Jesus the day he was visiting in Bethany at the home of Martha and her sister Mary. While Martha worked in the kitchen, Mary sat at Jesus' feet and listened to his teaching. But Martha was angry and said, "Lord, do you not care that my sister has left me to serve alone? Tell her then to help me."

But Jesus said, "Martha, Martha, you are anxious and troubled about many things; one thing is needful. Mary has chosen the good portion, which shall not be taken away from her."

Mary and Martha had a brother named Lazarus. One day, someone brought news to Jesus that Lazarus was dead. "Let us go to him," Jesus said to the disciples. But by the time they arrived in Bethany, Lazarus had been in the tomb for four days.

Martha ran to meet Jesus, saying, "If you had been here, my brother would not have died."

"Your brother will rise again," Jesus assured her.

"I know that he will rise again in the resurrection at the last day," Martha said.

"I am the resurrection and the life. Those who believe in me, though they die, yet shall they live, and whoever lives and believes in me shall never die. Do you believe this?" asked Jesus.

"Yes, Lord," said Martha, "I believe that you are the Christ."

Just then, Martha called to Mary. When Mary came from the house, she greeted Jesus with the same words Martha had used. When Jesus saw that she was weeping, and that her neighbors were weeping, too,

Jesus wept. Some people said, "See how Jesus loved him!" But others said, "Could not the one who opened the eyes of the man born blind have kept this man from dying?"

Jesus went to the cave where Lazarus lay and commanded, "Take away the stone."

Martha was amazed. "Lord, by this time there will be an odor, for he has been dead for four days!"

But Jesus reminded Martha, "Did I not tell you that if you would believe, you would see the glory of God?" Then he prayed and called, "Lazarus, come out." And Lazarus came out of the cave, his hands and feet still bound, and his face wrapped in a grave cloth.

Jesus said to the sisters, "Unbind him and let him go."

Jesus continued on his way toward Jerusalem, and as he passed through Jericho, a blind beggar named Bartimaeus called out, "Jesus, Son of David, have mercy on me!" The townspeople rebuked him, but Bartimaeus cried out all the more.

So Jesus stopped and said, "What do you want me to do for you?"

Bartimaeus said, "Teacher, let me receive my sight."

"Go your way," Jesus said, "your faith has made you well."

At that, Bartimaeus could see again, but instead of going home, he followed Jesus on the way.

In Jericho there was also a very rich chief tax collector named Zacchaeus. He, too, wanted to see Jesus, but could not because he was too short to see over the crowd. So he climbed up and sat in a sycamore tree. But when Jesus looked up, he said, "Zacchaeus, make haste and come down; for I must stay at your house today."

Joyfully, Zacchaeus came down from the tree and received Jesus into his home. But outside, the people were angry.

"Jesus has gone in to be a guest in the home of a man who is a sinner," they said.

Zacchaeus, however, said to Jesus, "Half of my goods I give to the poor; and if I defrauded anyone of anything, I restore it fourfold."

Jesus then told the crowd, "Today salvation has come to this house."

The time came for Jesus to enter Jerusalem. Years earlier, the prophet Zechariah had foretold that the Messiah would enter the city "humble and mounted on a donkey." So Jesus said to his disciples, "Go into the village opposite you, and immediately you will find a donkey tied, on which no one has ever sat; untie it and bring it to me. If anyone says to you, 'Why are you doing this?' you shall say, 'The Sovereign has need of it.'"

When they brought the donkey to Jesus, those who were with him spread their garments on it and on the road. Others spread leafy branches on the road and they shouted, "Hosanna! Blessed is the one who comes in the name of the Sovereign! Hosanna in the highest!"

But the Pharisees who heard this were shocked and ordered Jesus,

"Teacher, rebuke your disciples."

Jesus refused. "I tell you, if the disciples were silent, the very stones would cry out."

Then Jesus and the others entered the temple. When he saw the money changers and people selling pigeons, Jesus shouted, "It is written, 'My house shall be called a house of prayer,' but you make it a den of robbers." And he turned over their tables and chairs.

When the rulers of the temple saw this, they sought a way to destroy him. One of them tried to trap Jesus with a question. "Teacher, we know that you are true, and teach the way of God truthfully. Tell us, then, what you think. Is it lawful to pay taxes to Caesar, or not?"

"Show me the money for the tax," Jesus said. And when they did, he asked, "Whose likeness and inscription is this?"

"Caesar's," they said.

"Render therefore to Caesar," Jesus answered, "the things that are Caesar's and to God the things that are God's."

Jesus had avoided their trap and so the religious leaders began to discuss how they might have Jesus arrested secretly. Passover was beginning, and because of the crowds that would be coming to Jerusalem, the Romans would be on guard against disturbances of any sort. The rulers of the temple and synagogues did not want to upset the followers of Jesus and cause a riot. So they found a way to get to Jesus from inside his circle of friends. Judas Iscariot went to them and said:

"What will you give me if I deliver him to you?"

And they offered Judas thirty pieces of silver.

Jesus sensed that the end of his life and ministry was drawing near. Trying to reassure the disciples, Jesus told them stories of what the future might hold. One story went like this:

"When the Son of man comes in glory and rules from a glorious throne, all the peoples will be gathered. The Ruler will separate them from one another as a shepherd separates the sheep from the goats, placing the sheep on the right, and the goats on the left. Then the Ruler will say to those on the right, 'Come, O blessed ones, inherit the realm prepared for you from the foundation of the world. For I was hungry and you gave me food, I was thirsty and you gave me drink, I was a stranger and you welcomed me, I was naked and you clothed me, I was sick and you visited me, I was in prison and you came to me.' Then the righteous will answer him. 'Sovereign, when did we see you hungry and feed you, or thirsty and give you drink? And when did we see you a stranger and welcome you, or naked and clothe you? And when did we see you sick or in prison and visit you?' And the Ruler will answer them. 'Truly, I say to you, as you did it to one of the least of these my sisters and brothers, you did it to me.'"

When they returned to Bethany, a woman came to Jesus with an expensive flask of ointment, and she poured it on Jesus' head. The disciples disapproved.

"Why this waste?" they asked. "For this ointment might have been sold for a large sum, and given to the poor."

But Jesus said, "You always have the poor with you, but you will not always have me. In pouring this ointment on my body, she has done it to prepare me for burial. Truly, I say to you, wherever the gospel is preached in the whole world, what she has done will be told in memory of her."

On the first day of the Feast of Unleavened Bread, the beginning of Passover, the disciples asked Jesus, "Where will you have us prepare for you to eat the Passover?"

He answered, "Go into the city, and a man carrying a jar of water will meet you. Follow him, and wherever he enters, say to the householder, 'The Teacher says, Where is my guest room where I am to eat the passover with my disciples?' And the householder will show you a large upper room furnished and ready; there prepare for us."

When evening came, and all was ready, Jesus removed his garments and wrapped a towel around his waist. With water he had poured into a basin, he washed the disciples' feet and dried them with the towel.

"You shall never wash my feet!" protested Peter.

"If I do not wash you, you have no part in me," said Jesus. "If I then, your Sovereign and Teacher, have washed your feet, you also ought to wash one another's feet. For I have given you an example, that you also should do as I have done to you."

As they were at the table eating, Jesus said, "Truly, I say to you, one of you will betray me, one who is eating with me."

The disciples were sorrowful and began to ask, "Is it I?"

"It is he to whom I shall give this morsel," said Jesus. And he handed a piece of bread to Judas, saying, "What you are going to do, do quickly. The Son of man goes as it is written, but woe to that person by whom the Son of man is betrayed! It would have been better for that one not to have been born."

As they were eating, Jesus took bread, and blessed and broke it, and gave it to the disciples, and said, "Take, eat; this is my body."

Then he took a cup, and when he had given thanks he gave it to them, saying, "Drink of it, all of you; for this is my blood of the covenant, which is poured out for many for the forgiveness of sins."

The disciples were sad as they ate and drank, but Jesus comforted them, saying, "Let not your hearts be troubled; believe in God, believe also in me. In my Father's house are many rooms; if it were not so, would I have told you that I go to prepare a place for you? I will come again and will take you to myself, that where I am you may be also. And you know the way where I am going."

"Lord, we do not know where you are going; how can we know the way?" asked Thomas.

"I am the way, and the truth, and the life; no one comes to God, but by me," said Jesus. And he added, "The Counselor, the Holy Spirit, will teach you all things. My peace I give to you."

When they finished eating, they sang a Passover hymn and went out to the Mount of Olives.

"You will all fall away," Jesus told them, "for it is written, 'I will strike the shepherd, and the sheep will be scattered.' But after I am raised up, I will go before you to Galilee."

"Even though they all fall away, I will not," promised Peter.

But Jesus looked at him and said, "Truly, I say to you, this very night, before the cock crows twice, you will deny me three times."

"If I must die with you, I will not deny you," Peter protested again. And they all said the same.

"Sit here while I pray," Jesus said. Then taking only Peter and James and John, Jesus went farther into the garden.

"Keep watch," he said. And then he prayed: "My Father, if it be possible, let this cup pass from me; nevertheless, not as I will, but as you will." When he returned to his disciples, Jesus found them asleep.

"So you could not watch with me one hour? Watch and pray that you may not enter into temptation. The spirit indeed is willing, but the flesh is weak."

A second and a third time Jesus went off to pray and when he returned, he found the disciples asleep. "Are you still sleeping and taking your rest? Rise, let us be going. See, my betrayer is at hand."

The disciples looked up and saw a great crowd entering the garden. The chief priests and scribes and elders were there along with the temple guard. Many carried clubs. Judas had told them, "The one I shall kiss is the man; seize him." Now Judas came up to Jesus and said, "Hail, Teacher!" Then Judas kissed him.

Jesus said to Judas, "Friend, why are you here?" And the guards seized Jesus.

One of those with Jesus drew his sword and struck the high priest's slave, cutting off his ear.

"Have you come out as against a robber, with swords and clubs?" Jesus asked them. "When I was with you day after day in the temple, you did not lay hands on me. But let the scriptures be fulfilled."

The guards led Jesus to the house of Caiaphas, the high priest. A trial was begun. The chief priest and the whole council sought testimony against Jesus to put him to death. But they found none. The stories told by many witnesses did not agree.

"We heard him say, 'I will destroy this temple that is made with hands, and in three days I will build another, not made with hands.'"

Finally Caiaphas asked, "Are you the Christ?"

"I am," Jesus replied.

"Why do we still need witnesses?" asked the high priest. "You have heard his blasphemy. What is your decision?"

The members of the council said, "He deserves death." And they covered his face and spit on him and said, "Prophesy to us, you Christ! Who is it that struck you?"

Meanwhile, Peter was in the courtyard, warming himself by the fire. Suddenly a woman said, "You also were with Jesus the Galilean."

"I do not know what you mean," denied Peter.

A second woman agreed. "This man was with Jesus of Nazareth."

"I do not know the man," Peter insisted.

"Certainly you are also one of them, for your accent betrays you. You are a Galilean."

"I do not know this man of whom you speak," said Peter for a third time. Immediately a cock crowed. Peter, remembering what Jesus had said, went out and wept.

In the morning, Jesus was taken to Pilate.

"Are you the King of the Jews?" Pilate asked Jesus.

"You have said so," Jesus answered him. Then Jesus was silent. When the chief priests accused Jesus before Pilate, he made no answer.

"He stirs up the people," said the chief priests, "teaching throughout all Judea, from Galilee even to this place."

As soon as Pilate heard that he was a Galilean, he sent Jesus to be tried by the ruler of Galilee, King Herod. But once again, Jesus was silent, and Herod sent him back to Pilate.

When Pilate saw that Jesus had been returned, he said to the crowd, "You brought me this man as one who was perverting the people; and after examining him before you, I did not find Jesus guilty of any of your charges against him. Neither did Herod, for he has sent Jesus back to us. But you have a custom that I should release one man for you at the Passover. Do you want me to release for you the King of the Jews?"

The people shouted, "Not Jesus, but Barabbas!" Barabbas had been imprisoned on charges of murder, robbery, and insurrection. Pilate must have been shocked by the people's request.

"Then what shall I do with the one whom you call the King of the Jews?"

"Crucify him!" the people cried.

"Why, what evil has he done?"

They did not answer, but shouted all the more, "Crucify, crucify!"

Pilate asked for a bowl of water and washed his hands before the people. "I am innocent of this man's blood; see to it yourselves."

And so it was that Pilate turned Jesus over to the Roman soldiers. They beat him and put a scarlet robe on him and a crown of thorns. They bowed mockingly before him, saying, "Hail, King of the Jews."

Pilate had Jesus brought before the people again, and he said, "Here he is!"

"Crucify, crucify!" they shouted.

"Shall I crucify your King?" asked Pilate.

The chief priests answered, "We have no king but Caesar!"

The guards forced Jesus to carry his own cross as they led him away. When it became too heavy, a man named Simon of Cyrene carried it for him.

They took Jesus to Golgotha, a hill called "the place of the skull." The soldiers offered Jesus some wine, but he refused to drink it. And they crucified him, and then the soldiers cast lots for his garments. Someone put a sign over Jesus' head, and the inscription of the charge against him read "The King of the Jews."

From a distance the women watched: Mary, his mother; Mary Magdalene; Mary, the mother of James and Joseph; Salome, the mother of the sons of Zebedee; and yet another Mary, the wife of Clopas. When Jesus saw his mother standing with a disciple whom he loved, he said, "Woman, behold, your son!"

The people began to mock him again, saying, "If you are the King of the Jews, save yourself."

Two thieves were crucified beside Jesus, one on his right and one on his left. One said, "Are you not the Christ? Save yourself and us!" But the other thief said, "Do you not fear God, since you are under the same sentence of condemnation?"

And Jesus said to the second thief, "Truly, I say to you, today you will be with me in Paradise."

From the sixth to the ninth hour, the sky was dark. And when the ninth hour came, Jesus cried with a loud voice: "Eli, Eli, lama sabachthani?" which meant "My God, my God, why have you forsaken me?" When the people heard this, however, they said, "This man is calling Elijah."

Then Jesus said (to fulfill the scripture), "I thirst," and he was given some vinegar to drink.

When Jesus had received the vinegar he said, "It is finished." And as he died, the curtain in the temple which separated the people from the ark of God's covenant was suddenly torn in two from top to bottom.

Seeing this, the centurion said, "Truly, this man was the Son of God!"

Joseph of Arimathea, a member of the council who was also seeking God's realm, asked Pilate for Jesus' body; and in his own new tomb, Joseph buried Jesus. Then Joseph rolled a large, heavy stone before the door of the tomb.

On the first day of the week, in the morning, Mary Magdalene and the other women brought spices to the tomb to anoint Jesus' body. Suddenly they saw that the stone had been rolled away from the door of the tomb. They were filled with fear, but then they heard a young man say, "Do not be amazed; you seek Jesus of Nazareth, who was crucified. He has risen, he is not here; see the place where they laid him."

The women told the other disciples, who, having looked into the empty tomb, went home wondering. Mary Magdalene stayed in the garden but as she wept, she heard a voice say, "Woman, why are you weeping?"

"Because they have taken away my Lord, and I do not know where they have laid him," she replied.

"Whom do you seek?"

Thinking the man to be a gardener, Mary said, "Sir, if you have carried him away, tell me where you have laid him, and I will take him away."

"Mary," he said.

Suddenly recognizing that it was Jesus, Mary cried, "Rabboni."

Jesus said to her, "Do not hold me, for I have not yet ascended to God. Go to my friends and say to them that I am ascending to my God and your God."

Mary hurried back to the disciples, proclaiming the news: "I have seen the Lord."

Soon it was said that Jesus was also seen on the road to Emmaus, and in Jerusalem in the upper room (although Thomas doubted it until he saw with his own eyes). Jesus was even seen in Galilee beside the sea and the disciples reported that on a mountaintop in Galilee Jesus gave them the "Great Commission": "Go therefore and make disciples of all nations, baptizing them in the name of the Father and of the Son and of the Holy Spirit, teaching them to observe all that I have commanded you; and I am with you always, to the close of the age."

But Luke reported that the disciples saw Jesus for the last time near Jerusalem. Luke wrote: "Jesus said to them, 'These are my words which I spoke to you, while I was still with you, that everything written about me in the law of Moses and the prophets and the psalms must be fulfilled. But stay in the city, until you are clothed with power from on high.'" Then Jesus led them out as far as Bethany, and with hands uplifted, blessed them. In the middle of the blessing, Jesus parted from them, and was carried up into heaven. With great joy the disciples returned to Jerusalem, and they were continually in the temple blessing God.

Through Abraham, God had said that all nations would bless themselves. Now, as Jesus parted from the earth in the middle of a blessing, that blessing upon the people of faith would continue forever.

CHAPTER 12

LIBERATION

The disciples remained in Jerusalem. When the Jewish Feast of Pentecost came, they were all gathered in the upper room. Suddenly there was the sound of a mighty wind and on each head there appeared to be tongues of fire. All at once, the disciples began to speak and soon a large crowd gathered outside to hear what was going on. The people in Jerusalem that day had come from all parts of the Roman Empire for the festival, and they spoke many different languages. Yet they all said they understood what it was the disciples were saying. (Although others, seeing the disciples' joy, said that they must be drunk!)

Peter addressed the crowd, "Give ear to my words. These people are not drunk as you suppose, but this is what was spoken by the prophet Joel:

> 'And in the last days it shall be, God declares,
> that I will pour out my Spirit on all flesh,
> and your sons and your daughters shall prophesy,
> and your young shall see visions,
> and the old shall dream dreams.' "

Peter told the good news of Jesus, that Jesus was indeed the Messiah promised in the Scriptures. Many believed him, and the disciples baptized three thousand people that day.

Soon after, Peter and John went to the temple to pray. At the Beautiful Gate of the temple there sat a man who had been lame all his life. He stretched out his hand to the disciples, begging for money.

Peter said, "I have no silver and gold, but I can give you what I have; in the name of Jesus Christ of Nazareth, walk."

The man got up and walked, and as people gathered around to see, Peter told them what he had told the others at Pentecost, and many more believed in Jesus.

But when members of the Sanhedrin heard this, they had Peter and John arrested and brought before the council.

Peter testified, "Rulers of the people and elders, if we are being examined today concerning a good deed done to one who was lame, by what means this person has been healed, be it known to you all, and to all the people of Israel, that by the name of Jesus Christ of Nazareth, whom you crucified, whom God raised from the dead, by that name this person is standing before you well."

The council, realizing that there would be trouble if the disciples were punished, warned Peter and John never again to speak of Jesus. But the disciples said, "We cannot but speak of what we have seen and heard."

Soon the followers of Jesus began to live in one community together and to share all they had. They met regularly for prayer and to hear stories about Jesus. As the community grew, however, it became a threat to the leaders of the temple and the council. What if the Romans decided to destroy this new movement, they worried? Would the Romans not also destroy Judaism and the temple in the process? So, one day, after a follower named Stephen preached about Jesus, the council had him arrested and stoned him to death.

One of those responsible for the stoning was a Pharisee from Tarsus named Saul. Saul was so convinced that the followers would destroy Judaism that he was determined to destroy the followers first. He headed north to Damascus with the high priest's permission to arrest any followers and to bring them back to Jerusalem for trial. But on the road, Saul had a vision—first he saw a great light, then he heard a voice.

"Saul, Saul, why do you persecute me?"

"Who are you?" Saul asked, falling to the ground in fear.

"I am Jesus, whom you are persecuting. But rise and enter the city, and you will be told what you are to do."

When Saul arose, he opened his eyes but discovered that he had been completely blinded by the experience. Those who were traveling with him had to lead him into Damascus by the hand. For three days, Saul lay blind, until a follower of Jesus named Ananias, at God's command, laid hands on him and not only restored his vision but opened his eyes about Jesus. Saul was baptized. Perhaps that is when he gave up his Jewish name, Saul, and began to be known by its Roman counterpart, Paul.

Paul began to preach in the synagogues, saying, "Jesus is the Child of God!" And when he did, the authorities rose up against Paul even as he had risen up against the followers of Jesus. One night, when the authorities set out to arrest him, Paul's new friends helped him escape from Damascus by hiding him in a basket and lowering it down from the city walls.

While Paul was learning new things about Jesus, Peter was learning new things about how Jesus' followers should live. The Jewish people had always obeyed very strict laws about what to eat and what not to eat. (These laws had always prevented them from associating with non-Jews or Gentiles.) But one day, in a vision, Peter discovered that nothing which God had created could be called unclean. That very day, for the first time, Peter baptized a Gentile convert into the faith. When the others heard of this, they said, "Then to the Gentiles also God has granted repentance unto life."

The new faith spread. A man named Barnabas was sent to find Paul and take him to Antioch to preach and teach the faith. It was at Antioch that the followers were first called Christians.

But as the faith grew, so did opposition against it. The king Herod Agrippa executed James, the brother of John, and then arrested Peter. Helped by an angel of God, Peter escaped from prison, but from then on, there was little hope for the Christian way in Jerusalem.

One day, as Paul and the others were worshiping God and fasting, the Holy Spirit said, "Set apart for me Barnabas and Saul for the work to which I have called them." The followers prayed and fasted and sent the two out as the first missionaries of the gospel of Christ.

On their first missionary journey, Paul and Barnabas and a young man known as John Mark sailed first to Cyprus, then to Perga, and then on to Antioch in Pisidia. And there Paul, too, announced to the leaders of the synagogues that the gospel would be preached to Gentiles: "It was necessary that the word of God should be spoken first to you. Since you thrust it from you, we turn to the Gentiles. For so God has commanded us, saying,

> 'I have set you to be a light for the Gentiles,
> that you may bring salvation to the uttermost parts of the earth.'"

The apostles were run out of this town and the next. When they came to Lystra they were accepted at last, but for the wrong reasons.

In Lystra there was a man who had been lame from birth. Paul sensed, however, that he had the faith to be made well, so Paul commanded, "Stand upright on your feet." And the man stood up and walked. Suddenly, all who saw it began to talk excitedly in their native language. Then some of the local priests brought forward a pair of oxen with floral garlands around their necks and began to prepare a sacrifice. Finally Paul understood that he was being worshiped as the Roman god Hermes, while Barnabas was being mistaken for Zeus. Paul tore his clothes in sorrow and cried, "People, why are you doing this? We are human beings, like you, and bring you good news, that you should turn from these vain things to a living God." Just then, Jewish people from the first two towns arrived and convinced the crowd that Paul should be stoned to death. Paul and Barnabas quickly escaped and eventually set sail again for Antioch and home.

Soon the apostles from the north and the south met together in Jerusalem to decide once and for all whether or not a person needed to be a Jew before becoming a Christian. Silas was appointed to accompany Paul and Barnabas on their return trip to Antioch with this news: "It has seemed good to the Holy Spirit and to us to lay upon you no greater burden than these necessary things." They suggested some food laws and a moral way of life, but Gentile converts were to be accepted into the Christian way on faith alone and not because they had first been Jews.

Paul said to Barnabas, "Come, let us return and visit the brothers and sisters in every city where we proclaimed the word of God, and see how they are." Barnabas agreed, as long as John Mark could go with them. But, John Mark had left the first missionary journey before the work was done, and Paul did not want to take the risk of losing him again. The two apostles argued and finally separated. Barnabas and John Mark headed for Cyprus and Paul took Silas and departed through Syria and Cilicia.

In Lystra, Paul accepted as a fellow missionary a young Greek Jew named Timothy. And one night at Troas, Paul had a second vision—he saw a person from Macedonia, in Europe, and heard a voice begging, "Come over to Macedonia and help us." Believing this to be a summons from God, Paul immediately set sail for Philippi, a leading city of Macedonia. With him were Silas and a physician named Luke, the man credited with writing one of the Gospels and the book of Acts. There was a group of women in Philippi who gathered by the river for worship each sabbath. When the apostles heard about it they went to the river to worship with the women and to tell them about Jesus. Lydia, a woman of high standing and a dealer in purple dyes, believed what she heard and asked to be baptized that day. She said to Paul and the others, "If you have judged me to be faithful to the Sovereign, come to my house and stay." They did, and the church at Philippi was begun.

One day, as the apostles were going to the place of prayer by the river, a fortune teller approached them and began to chant, "These men are servants of the Most High God, who proclaim to you the way of salvation." It was said that the woman was filled with an evil spirit, and that her owners made much money from her predictions.

Paul, however, became annoyed by her constant shouting. He turned and spoke directly to the evil spirit, "I charge you in the name of Jesus Christ to come out of her."

At that moment, the evil spirit left the woman, but when her owners realized that she could no longer tell fortunes for money, they seized Paul and Silas and brought them before the Roman authorities, saying that they were disturbing the peace. The Romans had the two apostles whipped and thrown into jail.

That night, however, as Paul and Silas were singing hymns and praying, there was a great earthquake and all the doors suddenly came open. When the jailer heard of this, he ran to the prison preparing to kill himself if the prisoners had escaped.

"Do not harm yourself," Paul cried as the jailer approached, "for we are all here."

The jailer was amazed and relieved. Seeing the calm faith of the apostles, he threw himself at their feet and asked, "What must I do to be saved?"

Paul said, "Believe in the Lord Jesus, and you will be saved, you and your household." The jailor was baptized with his entire family.

In the morning, the apostles were released. They worshiped again with Lydia at the new church in her home. Of all the churches he founded, the church in Philippi was to be one of Paul's favorites. In later years, he sent the followers a loving letter in which he wrote one of the greatest statements of the Christian faith:

> "Have this mind among yourselves, which is yours in Christ Jesus who, though being in the form of God, did not count equality with God a thing to be grasped, but emptied Christ's self, taking the form of a servant, being born in the likeness of human beings. And being found in human form Christ humbled Christ's self and became obedient unto death, even death on a cross. Therefore God has highly exalted Jesus and bestowed on Jesus the name which is above every name, that at the name of Jesus every knee should bow, and every tongue confess that Jesus Christ is Sovereign."

From Philippi, Paul and Silas went on to Thessalonica, the capital of Macedonia, and then to Berea. In both towns, the Greeks listened to the apostles' message about Jesus, but the Jews questioned it. They criticized Paul for preaching about the freedom, or liberation, that the followers would have in Christ and for not preaching about their need to obey the law of Moses.

When Paul wrote to the Thessalonian Christians, he said, "We give thanks to God always for you all, constantly mentioning you in our prayers, remembering before our God your work of faith and labor of love and steadfastness of hope in our Sovereign Jesus Christ."

Silas, with Timothy, stayed in Berea while Paul traveled down to Athens. Athens was full of idols, for the Greeks worshiped many gods. There was even an altar "To an unknown god."

The people in Athens liked to debate one another in public, so Paul stood up in the middle of the marketplace and said, "People of Athens, I perceive that in every way you are very religious. The God who made the world, and everything in it, does not live in shrines made by human hands. The times of ignorance God overlooked, but now God commands all people everywhere to repent, because the day has been fixed on which God will judge the world in righteousness by a human being whom God has appointed, and of this God has given assurance to all by raising Jesus from the dead."

Although some believed (the books of Acts mentions that a man named Dionysius and a woman named Damaris heard Paul and believed), many laughed at the idea that anyone could be raised from the dead, so Paul left Athens and journeyed on to Corinth.

Corinth was an ancient Greek city that had been rebuilt as a Roman colony. Because it was a port city, it was known to be filled with every kind of crime and vice. Paul made good friends there, however, among them Priscilla and her husband, Aquila, tentmakers like himself. The leader of the synagogue, Crispus, soon became a follower, as did many others when they heard Paul's message. Silas and Timothy soon arrived from Macedonia and the apostles began a ministry in Corinth which would last for a year and a half. One night God assured Paul in a vision, "Do not be afraid, but speak and do not be silent. For I am with you and have many people in this city."

Again, there was trouble between Paul and Jews who followed strictly the law of Moses. His opponents tried to bring Paul before the Roman governor to be disciplined, but the governor declared, "If it were a matter of wrongdoing or vicious crime, I should have reason to bear with you, O Jews. But since it is a matter of questions about words and names and your own law, see to it yourselves." Paul left Corinth, but when he wrote the Corinthians the two letters now preserved in the Bible, he left words to inspire believers of all times and places:

> "If I speak in human tongues or the tongues of angels, but have not love, I am a noisy gong or a clanging cymbal. Love is patient and kind; love is not jealous or boastful; it is not arrogant or rude. Love bears all things, believes all things, hopes all things, endures all things. Love never ends. So faith, hope, love abide, these three; but the greatest of these is love."

After spending some time in Antioch in Syria, Paul set out on what is known as his third missionary journey, although he traveled less this time than on his earlier journeys. For three years he stayed in Ephesus, the capital of the Roman province of Asia. Ephesus, like Corinth, was a port city and was the geographic center of all the places to which Paul had traveled. It was also an important center for pagan worship.

An Ephesian silversmith named Demetrius was a maker of idols, silver models of the temple of the goddess Artemis. When Demetrius heard that Paul was preaching against idol worship, he called together all the idol-makers of the town, saying, "You know that from this business we have our wealth. And you see and hear that not only at Ephesus but almost throughout all Asia this Paul has persuaded and turned away a considerable company of people, saying that gods made with hands are not gods."

"Great is Artemis of the Ephesians!" cried the people.

A riot started, with more and more people shouting, "Great is Artemis!" Some wanted to arrest Paul, but the Christians helped him to escape from Ephesus. Before leaving them, Paul said, "You yourselves know how I lived among you, testifying both to Jews and to Greeks of faith in our Sovereign Jesus Christ. And now, I am going to Jerusalem, bound in the Spirit, not knowing what shall befall me there. I know that all you among whom I have gone preaching the realm will see my face no more."

In Jerusalem, Paul and Luke and those who traveled with them visited the Christian congregation, presenting to James an offering of money from the churches of Asia. But James warned Paul about the Jewish Christians of Jerusalem, "You see, brother, how many thousands there are among the Jews of those who have believed; they are all zealous for the law, and they have been told that you teach all the Jews who are among the Gentiles to forsake Moses, telling them not to circumcise their children or observe the customs. What then is to be done?"

It was decided that, in the morning, Paul and four converts should fulfill the law of Moses by going to the temple to purify themselves. Some of the Jewish Christians saw them and accused Paul of defiling the temple by bringing Gentiles into the inner court. They dragged Paul from the temple and would have killed him if Roman guards had not interfered and taken Paul to their commander.

From the steps of the Roman barracks, Paul addressed the Jewish people: "I am a Jew, born at Tarsus, educated according to the strict manner of the law of our ancestors. I persecuted this Way to the death, and I journeyed to Damascus to take those who were there and bring them in bonds to Jerusalem to be punished."

Then Paul recounted the vision of Jesus on the road and his work for the gospel among the Gentiles. But when he mentioned Gentiles, the mob shouted, "Away with him!"

The Romans put Paul in prison overnight but, because he was a Roman citizen, they did not punish him further. In the morning, he was delivered to the Sanhedrin where he was put on trial. The council could not agree what to do about Paul, so a group among them began secretly to plot his murder. When the Romans heard this, they escorted Paul by night back to Caesarea on the coast where his trial could be heard by the Roman governor, Felix.

Five days later, the members of the council arrived and brought accusation against Paul, but Felix, hoping that Paul would offer him some money as a bribe, ruled against the Sanhedrin and kept Paul in prison.

Two years passed. A new governor, Festus, took over in Caesarea. Again, some of the elders from Jerusalem came to accuse Paul, but this time Paul said, "I appeal to Caesar!" And Festus ruled, "You have appealed to Caesar; to Caesar you shall go."

Again accompanied by Luke, Paul set sail from Caesarea on a prison ship bound for Rome. Paul's ship was first becalmed by lack of wind and then tossed about in a terrible storm. Finally, near the island of Malta, the ship ran aground. Marooned on the island for three months, Paul preached the gospel to the inhabitants and healed them of their diseases. At last, when the weather cleared, a second ship took the prisoners to the end of their journey and, when Paul arrived in Rome, Christians from around the Empire greeted him with love and accompanied him as he walked the final few miles into the city.

Paul was again brought before the religious leaders for a hearing. Some believed in his words about Christ but some doubted. As a compromise, Paul was sentenced to house arrest, though for two more years it is said that he preached the gospel openly and unhindered. The Bible does not say how Paul died, but tradition suggests that when Nero was the emperor of Rome, Paul was executed.

The most beloved of Paul's letters is the one written to the Romans, in which Paul reassured them that, no matter what happened, his faith in Christ would always remain firm:

> "Who shall separate us from the love of Christ? Shall tribulation, or distress, or persecution, or famine, or nakedness, or peril, or sword? No, in all these things we are more than conquerers through the one who loved us. For I am sure that neither death, nor life, nor angels, nor principalities, nor things present, nor things to come, nor powers, nor height, nor depth, nor anything else in all creation, will be able to separate us from the love of God in Christ Jesus our Sovereign."

As the first century drew to a close, and as the Roman authorities began to persecute those who seemed to threaten Rome, many Christians witnessed to their faith by losing their lives. One, an elder named John, sought refuge on the island of Patmos. There he had a vision that one day God would again liberate the people and that never again would there be sorrow on the face of the earth. John wrote that as God had created all things in the beginning, so God would re-create all things again and would dwell with humankind forevermore:

"I saw a new heaven and a new earth; for the first heaven and the first earth had passed away, and the sea was no more. And I saw the holy city, new Jerusalem, coming down out of heaven from God, and I heard a loud voice say, 'The dwelling of God is with human beings. God will wipe away every tear from their eyes, and death shall be no more, neither shall there be mourning nor crying nor pain any more, for the former things have passed away.'"

"The grace of the Sovereign Jesus Christ be with the saints."

The Bread Book is based on selected passages from the following chapters and books of scripture.

Chapter 1: Genesis 1 to 3; 6 to 9:17

Chapter 2: Genesis 12 to 22

Chapter 3: Genesis 25, 27 to 33, 35, 37, 40 to 50

Chapter 4: Exodus 1 to 20, 24, 32, 34 to 36; Numbers 14, 27:12-23; Deuteronomy 34:1

Chapter 5: Joshua 1, 2, 6, 9, 24; Judges 4 to 8, 10, 13 to 16, 21; Ruth; 1 Samuel 1 to 3, 7, 8, 10, 16

Chapter 6: 1 Samuel 9, 16 to 18, 20, 24, 31; 2 Samuel 1, 3, 5 to 7, 11 to 13, 15, 16; 1 Kings 1, 2 to 5, 8 to 12

Chapter 7: 1 Kings 12, 14, 16 to 19, 21; 2 Kings 2, 9, 14, 17; Amos 5, 7; Isaiah 7, 11, 36, 37, 39

Chapter 8: Ezekiel 9, 34; Jeremiah 2, 7 to 9, 13, 18, 19, 27 to 29, 37, 38, 42 to 44; Psalms 119, 137; Isaiah 40, 45, 49, 53; Ezra; Haggai; Zechariah; Nehemiah

Chapter 9: Matthew 2 to 4; Luke 1, 2, 4

Chapter 10: Matthew 4 to 17; Mark 2, 4 to 8; Luke 5, 7, 8, 14; John 3, 4, 6

Chapter 11: Matthew 18, 19, 21, 22, 25 to 27; Mark 10, 11, 14 to 16; Luke 10, 15, 19, 23, 24; John 11, 13, 14, 19, 20

Chapter 12: Acts 2 to 4, 9, 11 to 14, 16 to 21; Philemon 2:5-11; 1 Thessalonians 1:2; 1 Corinthians 13; Romans 8:35-39; Revelation 1:9, 21:1-6, 22:21

INDEX